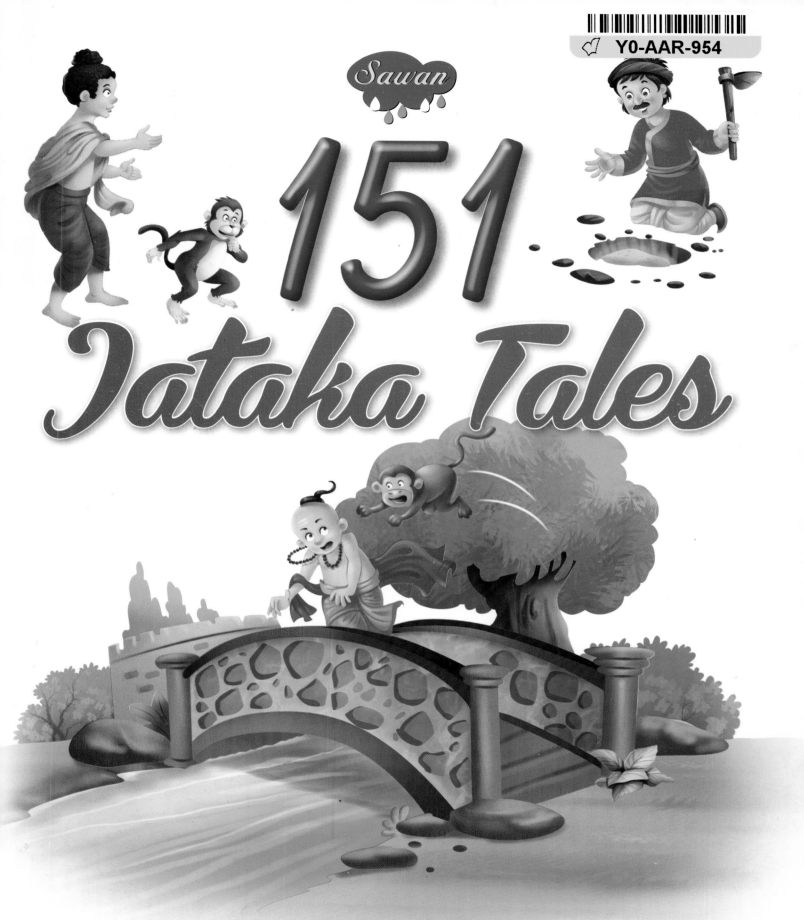

Sawan
151
Jataka Tales

Y0-AAR-954

151 *Jataka Tales*

Publisher:
MANOJ PUBLICATIONS

761, Main Road, Burari, Delhi-110084
Ph.   : 27611116, 27611349
Fax   : 27611546, Mob. : 9868112194
email   : info@manojpublications.com
For online shopping visit our website : **www.manojpublications.com**

Showroom :

1583-84, Dariba Kalan, Chandni Chowk, Delhi-110006
Ph. : 23262174, 23268216
Mobile : 9818753569

ISBN : 978-81-310-1886-6

CONTENTS

1. *The Varying Seasons*

Four princes had heard about a Red-Bud tree but not seen it.

One day, the eldest prince went into the woods to see it. It was spring and the tree had no leaves or buds. The prince could not understand why it was called a Red-Bud tree.

Then, during spring, the next son went to see the tree. This time it was covered with red buds.

Now, when the third son went to see the tree, it was covered with green leaves.

Finally, the youngest prince went to see the Red-Bud tree. By this time it was covered with little bean-pods.

He excitedly told the other princes, "I have seen the Red-Bud tree."

The others shouted, "We too!"

Each explained what he saw. Now, they got confused because each had seen a different shade of the tree.

The king hearing this, explained to them, "You have seen the same tree, but at a different time of the year."

2. The Clever Merchant and the What Not Tree

Once, a merchant was travelling with his caravan. They stopped near a village and camped for the night. Near their camp stood a tree which looked like a mango tree.

The merchant saw the tree and said to his servants, "This tree does look like a mango tree but it is a poisonous What Not tree. Do not eat its fruit!"

Unfortunately, some of his servants ignored the warning out of hunger. They ate the fruit and died.

The next day, some villagers came to the camp site expecting to see dead people but they were in for a surprise as the merchant and his men were alive.

They asked the merchant, "How it so happened that you are alive? Why did you not eat the fruit of this tree?"

The merchant replied, "I noticed that the fruit of this tree had not been plucked by anyone. Thus, there was something wrong with them. They were not to be eaten!"

Everyone appreciated the merchant's wisdom.

3. The Mosquito and the Foolish Son

Once there was a carpenter. He was working hard. Now, the carpenter was bald. A mosquito seeing the shiny bald head of the carpenter went and sat on his head. It started biting the carpenter's head. The carpenter got irritated and chased the mosquito away with his hand but the mosquito came back. The carpenter again chased the mosquito with his hand. The mosquito went away but was persistent. It kept coming again and again. The carpenter was finally very tired.

He called out to his son, "Son, please get rid of this mosquito for me."

The son was very obedient but foolish. He hit the mosquito with a stick. Though the mosquito flew away yet the carpenter was wounded badly.

4. The Farmer and the Gold

Once, in a village, a rich man buried his gold in a field to keep it safe from thieves.

Years passed by. The rich man died. One day, a poor farmer who owned the field was ploughing it. While ploughing, his plough hit something hard.

At first the farmer thought it to be a stone. But he was amazed to see a lump of gold there. He decided to carry the gold home at night lest somebody should see him during the day.

At night, the farmer tried to lift the gold, but it was too heavy. Then he tried to drag it but it did not budge an inch.

Then he sat down to think as to how to move the gold. He decided to break it into four parts. Then he could carry home one piece at a time.

He did exactly that and carried the gold home easily.

He lived a wealthy man.

5. The King's Grey Hair

Long ago, people lived much longer than they do today.

Once, a king was more than a 1,000 years old. One day, he told the royal barber, "If you see any grey hair on my head, you must tell me immediately!" The barber agreed.

When the king was 1,500 years old, the royal barber said, "I see one grey hair on your head."

On hearing this, the king called his eldest son and made him the king.

His ministers were surprised and asked him why he was retiring.

The king held up the grey hair and said, "I have realized that this grey hair shows that death is approaching fast. I have wasted my precious life in seeking the pleasures of wealth and comfort. Now, I will meditate and attain wisdom."

He went into the forest and meditated hard. He became a great sage.

6. *The Lazy Student*

Once, a sage sent his students to the forest to gather firewood.

One of them was very lazy. He found a tree with no leaves. He thought, 'I am lucky. It will be easy to break the branches without having to break the leaves first. There is no need to hurry now.' He decided to take sleep for some time.

It was evening by the time he woke up. The other students were getting ready to go back with their wood.

He quickly started breaking the branches but discovered that they were actually still green and not dry. Despite that, he carried the wood back to the hermitage.

The next day, the cook lit the same wood. But alas! The wood would not burn. As a result, the breakfast was delayed. The students had to miss out on an important meeting due to this.

They told the sage everything.

The sage replied, "A fool who is lazy causes trouble for everyone."

7. *The Calves and the Pig*

Once, there were two calves and a baby pig in a farmhouse.

The pig was given the best of everything to eat while the two calves were given only grass and hay.

One of the calves complained about this to the other.

The other calf was wise. He said, "It is dangerous to envy anybody. The pig is being fed rich food because he will be served at a wedding that is to take place here."

Sure enough, on the wedding day, the pig was taken away to be served to the people.

The wise calf said, "Did you see what happened? Our poor grass and hay are a hundred times better than the rich food the pig was given. Our food brings no harm to us, but instead promises long life!"

8. The Clever Jackal

A jackal used to go to the neighbouring village and steal food from there. The villagers realised that someone was stealing their food. They laid a trap for the thief. The next day, when the jackal came to steal the food, he got trapped. With great difficulty, he was able to free himself and ran away. But by then, the villagers were on his tail.

The jackal hid in a cave. He could hear the villagers searching around. Suddenly, he saw a sage coming towards him.

The jackal called out to him and said, "My dear good sage! I am injured. Please carry me home."

The unsuspecting sage agreed and picked up the jackal.

After a few minutes, the jackal screamed, "Help! This sage is kidnapping me. He is the food thief."

The villagers saw the sage and caught him. The jackal, in the meanwhile, ran away.

The sage decided not to trust anyone blindly.

9. The Crow Couple and the Sea

Once, a crow and his wife were sitting near the sea. Suddenly, a big wave came and swept the crow's wife away. The crow cried and cried over the loss of his wife.

Soon, many crows gathered near him after hearing his cries. They asked him why he was crying. The crow told them everything. The crows felt very sad for the crow.

The crow decided to fast near the sea. He said, "I will not eat or sleep till I get my wife back."

Many days passed by but the crow did not give up his fasting. The sea-god was seeing all this. He felt pity for the crow and thought, 'He really does love his wife a lot.'

So impressed was the sea-god that he returned the crow's wife. The crow was very happy and thanked the sea-god.

10. The Drunken Beetle

Once, a beetle saw a pot of beer. Droplets of beer were scattered everywhere. The beetle enjoyed licking the drops. He was completely drunk by then. Then he crawled to the river-bank. By mistake, he fell on a dung heap.

At that very moment, an elephant came to the river to drink water. Seeing the drunken beetle covered with dung, the elephant lifted his trunk in disgust and backed away.

When the beetle saw this, he thought, 'That elephant is afraid of me! See how he backs off. I will fight him!' So he challenged the elephant to a fight. The elephant ignored him.

But the beetle started insulting the elephant. He shouted, "Hey you! You coward! Are you afraid of fighting me? I know I can defeat you easily."

The elephant got very angry. He dropped some more dung on the beetle and went away laughing.

11. The Wise Crab and the Crane

Once, it did not rain for a long time. A pond, where many fish and a crab lived, had very little water left. All the fish became worried.

They held a meeting. One wise fish said, "We need to move to another place where there is plenty of water."

A crane, who was hearing all this, said, "I know of a pond full of water. I can take you there."

No one trusted the crane, so the wise fish went with him to see the pond. He was delighted to see so much water and told everyone about it.

It was decided that the crane would take the fish to the new pond.

Every day, the crane took one fish. But, alas! He ate the fish on the way.

Finally, only the crab was left.

As the crab was going with the crane, he saw many fish bones scattered on the way. The clever crab realised what the crane had done.

He immediately clutched the crab's neck with his claws and killed him.

12. The Snake Charmer and the Monkey

Once, a snake charmer lived in a small village. He owned a few snakes and a monkey. He travelled across the villages and made these animals perform various tricks to earn his living.

But, the snake charmer was very cruel to his pets. He would never give them enough to eat and often beat them.

One day, the snake charmer beat his monkey badly for no reason. The monkey ran away and did not come back.

The snake charmer continued to hold the shows. People did not like his show now. He was not able to earn much. He understood that people liked his show because of the monkey.

The snake charmer searched for the monkey everywhere and found him sitting on a tree. He said with teary eyes, "My dear monkey, I missed you." "You have come here because people don't like your show now. That is why you miss me," the monkey replied and vanished.

The snake charmer realised his mistake and became kind to his pets.

13. The Miser

Once there was a Brahmin. He was a great miser. He had a son whom he loved very much.

When the son turned sixteen, he got very sick. The father being a miser did not send for a physician. He treated the boy himself. But the boy's condition got worse. Now, the miser feared that people would come to see his son and also see his wealth. So, he placed his son in the courtyard for people to see him.

A great sage came to see the son. He gave many sermons to the son. After some days, the son passed away. The miser mourned for his son's loss. He used to go to the funeral ground every day and weep for his son.

God was watching all this. He came down and spoke to the miser. He said, "Why do you mourn for your son? It is because of your miserliness that you lost him."

The miser realised his mistake and became very generous after that.

14. *The Priest's Revenge*

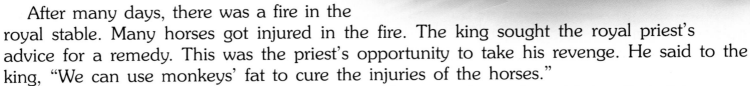

A king had an orchard. Many monkeys used to live there. One day, the royal priest was passing through the orchard. A naughty monkey made fun of him. The priest got angry and vowed to take revenge on all the monkeys.

The monkey king got worried. He told the monkeys to leave the orchard as they were in danger. Many monkeys agreed and left but a few stubborn ones did not leave.

After many days, there was a fire in the royal stable. Many horses got injured in the fire. The king sought the royal priest's advice for a remedy. This was the priest's opportunity to take his revenge. He said to the king, "We can use monkeys' fat to cure the injuries of the horses."

The king gave order to kill all the monkeys living in the park and bring their fat.

Thus, all those monkeys, who had ignored the advice of their king, died.

15. *The Values of Life*

Once, there was a rich man. But despite being rich he always believed that happiness could be obtained by leading a good life; money was not everything. He had a son. He wanted to teach his son the same thing.

One day, his son, while playing, broke his toy. The son started crying. His father came and consoled him. Then he said to his son, "Do not cry over this broken toy. Things come and go in life but the most important things in life are good health, truthfulness and sincerity. Never give up these values ever in your life."

The boy listened attentively to his father. He started leading a good life. When he grew up, he became very successful. He realized that his father's words were the reason behind his success.

16. The Goose with Golden Feathers

Once, there was a goose with golden feathers. She lived in a pond. Near this pond lived a poor woman with her two daughters.

The goose thought, 'If I give them my golden feathers, they will live happily.'

The goose went there and told the poor woman about this.

After this, the goose started shedding one feather every day.

The mother and her daughters bought eatables and other things every day. But, one day, the mother became greedy.

When the goose came, the mother grabbed her and pulled out all her feathers. But, the golden feathers changed into some strange feathers. The mother was shocked.

The goose said, "I wanted to help you, but you became greedy. Now, I will go away and never come back."

The mother felt sad and apologized for her actions. The goose advised, "Never be greedy again" and flew away.

17. The Hare's Sacrifice

Have you ever noticed the full moon? Well, we can see a mark on the moon which looks like a hare. Here is an interesting story about it.

Once, a hare had three friends - a monkey, an otter and a jackal. One day, the hare said to his friends, "Let us do some charity. If we give alms, we will be blessed."

All the friends brought something to give for charity.

The hare, being small, could find nothing. He decided to give himself away in charity.

God heard this. He came disguised as a sage and asked the hare for food.

The hare offered himself. He lit up a fire and jumped into it. But God saved him.

He said to the hare, "You will be remembered for your sacrifice for ages to come."

Saying this, God drew a hare in the moon. It is still there for all to see.

18. The Mouse and the Stone-Cutter

Once, a rich man's wife was reborn as a mouse. She was so attached to her riches that even after becoming a mouse, she kept all the treasure near her.

Now, there was a stone-cutter. The mouse became his friend. The mouse gave him some money to buy food. From then on, the stone-cutter bought food for the mouse every day.

Once, a cat caught the mouse. The mouse offered to give the cat food every day in return for her freedom. The cat agreed.

Soon, the cat started eating a major share of the food. The mouse became weak.

The stone-cutter asked the mouse about this.

The mouse told him everything. The stone-cutter made a plan. He put the mouse inside a glass box. As soon as the cat jumped upon the box, the glass broke and pierced the cat. The cat died instantly. The mouse was free. Then the mouse gave her treasure to the stone-cutter in return for her help.

19. The Quail's Revenge

In a forest, there lived some quails. One day, one of the quails laid some eggs.

The quails came to know that an elephant was on a rampage in that area. Soon, the elephant came to the place where the quails lived. The mother quail begged the elephant, "Please spare my young ones!"

But the elephant did not listen to the quail and destroyed her eggs.

The mother wanted revenge. She called her friends - the crow, the ant and the frog, and came up with a plan.

First, the crow plucked out the elephant's eyes. Then the ant started biting the elephant. The elephant could not bear the pain and searched for water to wash his eyes. At the same time, the frog croaked close to a steep cliff. The elephant, thinking there was water near by, followed the sound of the frog's croaking. But, the elephant fell into the valley and died. The quail had got her revenge.

20. The Disciple's Faith

Long ago, Lord Buddha used to give sermons to his disciples in a monastery. One day, one of his disciples, who was coming to the monastery to hear his sermons, got late. On the way, he had to cross a river. But due to being late, he missed the boat.

The disciple was so engrossed in the Buddha's thoughts that unknowingly he stepped into the river. He kept saying to himself, "I do not want to miss Lord Buddha's sermon." He kept walking and walking. His thoughts were only on Lord Buddha.

Suddenly, when he was in the middle of the river, he realised that he was waist-deep in water. His concentration broke and he started panicking.

Then, once again, he started thinking of Lord Buddha. Slowly, all his fear vanished. Lo and behold! He crossed the river without any hassle. He reached the monastery and told everyone about how his faith in the Buddha had helped him.

21. The Pigeon and the Crow

A rich man had a bird house in which there lived a pigeon. The pigeon never entered the rich man's kitchen, for the cook was very cruel.

One day, a crow smelled the delicious food being cooked in the rich man's kitchen. He decided to befriend the pigeon, and thereby, enter the rich man's kitchen.

So, the next day, the crow became friends with the pigeon and moved into his bird house.

The crow observed the cook making a fish stew. His mouth watered.

The pigeon warned him, "Stay away from the kitchen or you will regret it!"

But the crow paid no attention.

He flew into the kitchen and picked up a fish. The cook saw him and trapped the crow. He plucked all the feathers of the crow and let him go. The pigeon was shocked to see the terrible state of the crow. He said, "You should have listened to me. Greed got the better of you."

22. The Silly Argument

Once, there were two friends - a lion and a tiger. They lived happily together. Not far from where they lived, dwelt a hermit.

One day, the two friends got into a silly argument. The tiger said, "It becomes cold when the moon decreases from full to new."

The lion replied, "No. It becomes cold when the moon increases from new to full."

The argument gave way to a quarrel. Then, suddenly, both thought that they would become enemies if they continued to fight. So, they stopped fighting. They decided to go and ask a learned hermit about this.

The hermit thought for a while and said, "It is the wind that brings the cold, not the moon. Do not destroy your friendship over silly arguments. Always remain united."

The lion and the tiger understood what the hermit meant. They thanked him and lived happily thereafter as good friends.

23. The Sage Who Sacrificed Himself

Once, a sage and his disciple were going through the forest. They chanced to see a tigress. She was going to kill her own cubs out of hunger.

The sage was saddened to see this. He decided to sacrifice himself. He sent his disciple to get some food lest he should object to the sage's actions. When the disciple had gone away, the sage went and stood in front of the tigress. The tigress and her cubs lost no time in attacking the sage and feasting on him.

When the disciple returned, he could not find the sage anywhere. He was surprised to see that the tigress no longer looked hungry. Her cubs were also playing around. Then, he saw the bloodstained clothes of the sage and understood what had taken place. Now he knew that the sage had sacrificed himself to feed a hungry tigress and protected her young ones as an act of great charity.

24. The Lean Cat

A woman had a pet cat but she was very lean as the woman was poor and gave little food to the cat. One day, the lean cat saw a healthy stray cat passing by. She was surprised to see such a healthy cat. She asked her, "How it so happened are so well fed?" The healthy cat replied, "I go to the palace and steal the tasty food that is spread out on the table." The lean cat's mouth started watering as she heard this and decided to go to the palace herself. Her master warned her not to go when she came to know about her plan. But the cat did not listen. The next day, she went inside the palace and grabbed a chicken piece. But as soon as she did this, the cook saw her and gave her a beating. The hurt cat went running back to her master.

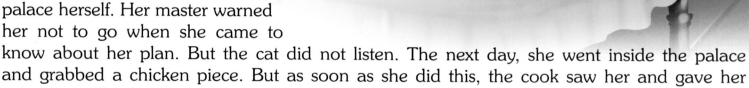

25. The Clever Wolf

Some men went to the forest for a picnic in the afternoon. But the walk to the forest was very tiring. So, they hurriedly ate up everything they had brought. After that, they all went off to sleep. It was dusk when they got up. All of them started feeling hungry again. One of them said, "Prepare fire. I will get something to eat." He took a club and reached a lake where animals came to drink water. He sat down under a tree and pretended to sleep. After some time, a pack of wolves came to drink water. They saw the man sleeping. The leader of the pack was clever. He told the other wolves, "This man is not sleeping. He is waiting to catch an animal." To prove his point, he went near the man. The man immediately got up and threw his club at the wolf. But the wolf was alert and dodged the club, and ran away.

26. The Selfish Ascetic

An ascetic lived in a mango grove near a river. But he had no qualities of an ascetic. He was very selfish and greedy. His main aim was to protect the mangoes and eat them.

God saw the doings of the ascetic. So, he decided to teach him a lesson.

One day, when the ascetic had gone to the village for alms, God destroyed the mango grove. The ascetic was shocked and furious to see his mangoes destroyed. He wanted to catch whoever had done that. At that moment, he saw four girls passing by. He caught them and accused them of destroying the grove. The girls swore innocence. The ascetic had to let them go. But the girls started crying as they felt humiliated.

God did not like this. He appeared before the ascetic and gave him a terrible scare. The terrified ascetic took to his heels and never returned there.

27. The Kind Tortoise

Long ago, some merchants were on a voyage. Suddenly, a great storm brewed up in the sea. It tossed the ship from left to right. The ship could not withstand the storm and sank. The merchants struggled in the water to stay alive. A turtle saw them struggling. He decided to help them. He went to the merchants and told them to climb on his back. The merchants climbed on his back and the tortoise took them safely to the shore. The merchants thanked the tortoise for his help. After a while, the merchants felt hungry. They discussed among themselves about the availability of food. The tortoise overheard their conversation. He felt sorry for them and decided to sacrifice himself. He went to the merchants and said, "You can have me as your food."

The merchants were deeply touched by this offer. They said to the tortoise, "We cannot kill you, for you have saved us."

Saying so, they patted the tortoise and left.

28. The Goat and the Priest

Once, a priest decided to sacrifice a goat. He thought God would be pleased.

When the priest was about to sacrifice the goat, it started laughing and crying at the same time.

The priest was baffled. He asked the goat the reason for this strange behaviour.

The goat replied, "Many births ago, I was a priest like you and sacrificed a goat. For that sin, I have been sacrificed in my so many rebirths. Today, I will be free.

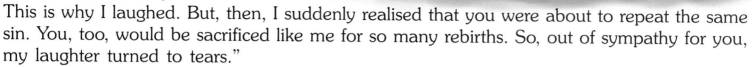

This is why I laughed. But, then, I suddenly realised that you were about to repeat the same sin. You, too, would be sacrificed like me for so many rebirths. So, out of sympathy for you, my laughter turned to tears."

The priest realised that the goat was right. He freed the goat and decided to please God by meditating instead.

29. The Drummers

A drummer and his son went to a fair to earn money by playing their drums. They earned a lot of money and were greatly applauded. While returning home, they had to cross a forest. Now, many thieves dwelled in that forest.

The boy thought, 'I will beat the drums to scare the thieves.' He started beating his drums loudly. But his father said, "Beat the drums in such a way that the thieves think that a royal procession is on the way with heavy security."

But the boy ignored his father's advice and kept beating the drums as he was doing earlier.

The thieves heard the drums and knew that it was not a big procession. They immediately attacked the father and the son and robbed them of their money.

The father was very angry. He told the son, "If only you had listened to me." The son was very ashamed of himself.

30. The Kind Ape

Once, an ape lived in a forest. He was very kind and virtuous.

One day, a shepherd lost his way and reached the forest. While finding his way out of the forest, he fell into a deep pit. The ape saw this and rescued him.

But in the process, the ape got weary. He fell into a deep sleep. The shepherd thought, 'I will kill this ape, take away his skin and sell it.'

He picked up a large stone and dropped it on the ape's head to kill him. Though the stone missed the ape yet he got up. The ape was hurt by the shepherd's actions and said, "I helped you but you wanted to kill me. God saved me because of my good deed."

The shepherd felt ashamed of his actions. He apologised to the ape. The ape forgave him and took him safely to his home.

31. The Talking Deer

Once, a deer lived deep in the jungle. But he was no ordinary deer, for he was very strong and wise, and spoke like a human.

One day, a king, who was hunting, saw this deer. The deer saw the king aiming his bow and arrow at him. He started running. The king followed him in hot pursuit.

The king was so bent on chasing the deer that he did not notice a great hollow in the earth. The deer jumped easily over it but the king fell into it.

The deer saw this.

Moved by compassion, he decided to help the king.

He said in a human voice, "I hope Your Majesty has not got hurt. I will take you out."

The king was astonished to hear the deer speaking. He realised that the deer was not ordinary.

The deer helped the king out of the hollow. The king was ashamed of his actions and sought the deer's forgiveness.

32. The Serpent King and the Saint

Two brothers were saints.

Now, there was a serpent king. He had a wish-fulfilling gem and could assume any form.

One day, he changed into a human and came to the hermitage of the brothers. He met the younger brother and became his friend. After that, he visited the brother frequently.

One day, the serpent visited the brother in his snake form. The brother was terrified. After that his health deteriorated. His brother noticed this and asked him the reason. The younger brother told him everything.

The elder brother said, "Ask the snake for his most valuable possession which is the gem. He will not part with it and stop coming to you."

So, the saint asked the serpent for his gem. The serpent king did not say anything and left. After this, the saint kept asking for the gem every day.

The serpent finally said, "You ask for too much. I will never visit you again."

The serpent went away and never came back.

33. The Ascetic Who Brought a River

There was a rich man who had a son. When the son grew up, he gave up his home and became an ascetic. He achieved great powers through meditation. Slowly, he obtained a large number of disciples. There were times when the ascetic would risk his life for the sake of his people. Once, a severe famine struck the land. Many creatures died of hunger and thirst. The ascetic was very upset. He meditated for several days. Due to his hard penances, he brought a river in the land. The people were shocked and happy. They realised that the ascetic was a divine being with great powers. They thanked the ascetic profusely.

The ascetic became famous everywhere. Many people came to listen to his sermons. He taught the people to be unselfish and make sacrifices for others.

One day, the ascetic fell ill. But such was his greatness that God himself came to cure him.

34. The Pigeons and the Fake Hermit

A king of pigeons used to visit a hermit every day and listen to his sermons. One day, the hermit left his hut and went away forever.

Many days later, a fake hermit came to live in the same hut. He was very fond of pigeon meat. One day, he saw a flock of pigeons near his hut. His mouth watered. He planned to kill and cook the pigeons.

So, the next day, he started the cooking process by putting in all the spices. Soon, the pigeons came flying. But their king smelt the spices and warned all the pigeons to stay away from the hut.

The hermit realised that his plan had been discovered. He threw a stick to hurt the pigeon king, but it missed him.

The pigeon king shouted, "You will suffer in hell for your sins. I will also reveal your true identity to everyone."

Frightened of the threat, the fake hermit left the hut and ran away.

35. The Three Princes and the Fairy

A king had three sons. The first two were from his previous queen. The stepmother wanted the king to make her son the king, but he refused.

The king was scared that the queen would harm his sons, so he told them to live in the forest until his death.

As they were going out of the palace, the youngest prince also joined them.

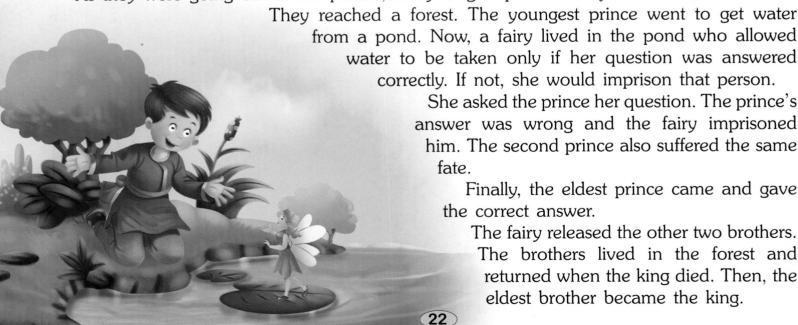

They reached a forest. The youngest prince went to get water from a pond. Now, a fairy lived in the pond who allowed water to be taken only if her question was answered correctly. If not, she would imprison that person.

She asked the prince her question. The prince's answer was wrong and the fairy imprisoned him. The second prince also suffered the same fate.

Finally, the eldest prince came and gave the correct answer.

The fairy released the other two brothers. The brothers lived in the forest and returned when the king died. Then, the eldest brother became the king.

36. The Disobedient Student

There was a famous teacher. He had many students. Among them was a student named Bhanu. He was not a good student. He was very disobedient. Bhanu never paid attention to what his teacher said. His main aim was to eat food and fight with his fellow students.

The teacher was fed up of Bhanu and his ways. One day, he threw Bhanu out of his hermitage.

Bhanu had nowhere to go now. He kept walking and walking till he came to a village. There he became a labourer to earn his livelihood.

After a while news spread that Bhanu was a student of a famous teacher. The villagers started seeking his advice. But after some time, the villagers felt that the advice that Bhanu gave was affecting them badly. They drove Bhanu away from their village. Bhanu repented being a bad student and not obeying his teacher.

37. The Water Spring

A certain merchant was leading his caravan to another country to sell his goods. Along the way, they came to a hot desert. It was so hot that the merchant's men started fainting. There was no water left. Some men started crying out of desperation.

The merchant thought, 'I must not give up. If I give up, my men will surely give up. I must be positive!'

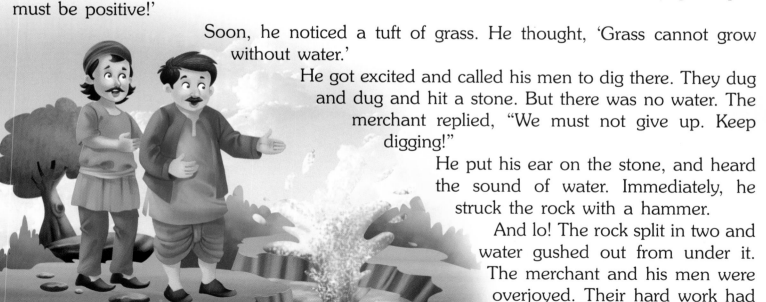

Soon, he noticed a tuft of grass. He thought, 'Grass cannot grow without water.'

He got excited and called his men to dig there. They dug and dug and hit a stone. But there was no water. The merchant replied, "We must not give up. Keep digging!"

He put his ear on the stone, and heard the sound of water. Immediately, he struck the rock with a hammer.

And lo! The rock split in two and water gushed out from under it. The merchant and his men were overjoyed. Their hard work had paid off.

38. The Brave Prince

A prince was very kind and generous. He always used to distribute his wealth among the poor people. One day, he decided to get more wealth.

Now, he had heard about a gem which could fulfil everyone's wishes. It was in a faraway land. The prince set off to get the gem.

It was a very long journey. Finally, the prince arrived there. The people did not like him. However, he did not lose heart. He met the king. The king told him that his kingdom was in trouble. A giant was troubling them. The prince said, "I will kill the giant but you will have to give me the gem in exchange." The king agreed.

The prince fought with the giant and killed him. The king gave the prince the gem.

The prince came back to his kingdom. From then on, no one was poor or unhappy as the wish-fulfilling gem fulfilled everyone's needs.

39. The Man with a Golden Heart

There was a rich man. This rich man was very generous. He used to give alms to the poor. Nobody returned empty-handed from his doorstep. He became very famous because of his generous ways. The gods were seeing everything. They were very impressed by the rich man and his ways.

But the king of gods said, "Let us test him. Will he be as generous when he is poor?"

So, the Gods disguised themselves as thieves and robbed the rich man of his riches.

The rich man became very poor.

One day, the king of gods came disguised as a beggar and begged for food. The rich man had only one piece of bread which he was eating. But, he quickly without hesitating gave it to the beggar.

The king of gods was very happy with the rich man. He immediately returned all his riches.

40. The King and the Ascetic

Once, a man became an ascetic. His wife happily accompanied him wherever he went. Many years passed by.

One day, a king was passing by where they lived. He was attracted to the ascetic's wife.

The king thought of carrying her away. But first, he wanted to know what the ascetic would do if he took the wife away.

In order to examine the powers of the ascetic, the king asked, "What would you do if a thief or a wild animal attacked your wife?"

The ascetic replied, "I would not release him."

The king thought that the ascetic was harmless and had no powers. He quickly dragged the wife towards his chariot.

Suddenly, the king had a thought. He came and asked the ascetic, "Whom did you refer to as 'him'?"

The ascetic replied, " 'Him' meant 'anger'." Then, the ascetic preached the king about the flaws of anger.

The words of the ascetic changed the king. He begged the ascetic's forgiveness and returned his wife.

41. Generosity Defeats Death

Once upon a time, a rich man was famous for his generosity.

In those days, a sage was meditating in the forest. While meditating, he remained without eating or drinking.

When he returned to his ordinary state, he was in danger of dying from starvation. So, he went to the rich man to get food.

Now, the god of death was watching all this. When he saw that the sage was near death from starvation, he decided to take him to his abode.

And so before the rich man could give food to the sage, the god of death caused a deep pit of red hot burning coals to appear between them.

But the rich man was not afraid. He crossed the burning pit and remained unharmed. Then he gave food to the sage. The god of death was defeated. He was amazed at the power of generosity.

42. *Land of Chaos*

Once, in a certain kingdom, people were immoral. There was chaos everywhere. Thieves grew in number. Well, the king too had strayed from his path.

Now, God was watching all this from heaven. He disliked what he saw. He wanted to teach those people a lesson. So, he disguised himself as a forester and took a fierce dog with him to the kingdom.

The dog barked so terribly outside the kingdom that the people got terrified and ran helter-skelter in fear.

The king ran out to see what the entire ruckus was about. He saw the forester standing with his dog. The fierce look of the dog scared the king too.

The forester said to the king, "My dog is hungry and will eat everyone who has sinned."

The king got scared and so did the people. He begged for forgiveness.

Then, God revealed his true identity. The people as well as the king promised never to commit sin.

43. *The Disciple's Wife*

Once, a teacher had a disciple who was from the countryside. He fell in love with a city girl and married her.

But after some days, the disciple found out that his wife was very moody. When she was in a good mood, she was very sweet to him but when she was in a bad mood, she insulted him.

The disciple was so disturbed that he stayed away from classes.

When he finally showed up, the teacher asked, "You have been away so long. What is the matter?"

He replied, "Sir, I am troubled by my wife's behaviour."

The teacher replied, "It is hard to understand why some people act the way they do. Accept your wife the way she is. Treat her in the same understanding way, whether she is kind or mean to you."

The student followed the teacher's advice. His wife's behaviour no longer upset him. His wife, too, changed her ways slowly due to her husband's understanding ways.

44. The Brahmin and the Wise Ascetic

Once, an ascetic was taking a walk in the city when he saw something strange.

He saw a Brahmin running very fast with a very expensive piece of cloth in his hand.

The ascetic asked him, "My dear friend! Where are you going in such a hurry?"

The Brahmin replied, "Sir! I am going to the funeral ground to burn this cloth."

The ascetic was surprised to hear this. He asked, "Why?"

The Brahmin replied, "Today morning, I saw that some rats were biting my cloth. I realised that this was a bad omen for me. I have to get rid of this cloth. "

The ascetic said, "You should not believe in such omens. The rats bit the cloth because they must have felt hungry."

The Brahmin replied, "Oh! I never thought about that. Thank you for opening my eyes, Sir. From now on, I will not fall for such omens."

45. The King's Sacrifice

King Vessantara was very famous for his generosity.

When he was a baby, a young white elephant had been brought to the palace. The prince and the elephant grew up together. Many people said that the kingdom was prosperous because of the presence of the white elephant.

One day, Vessantara lent the elephant to the neighbouring kingdom because it was passing through a bad phase.

But the people of Vessantara's kingdom were very angry at this. Vessantara was banished from the kingdom. While leaving, Vessantara gave away all his possessions.

Hearing of his charity, a poor Brahmin came to ask for Vessantara's children to be his servants. Vessantara immediately gave away his beloved children.

God wanted to test Vessantara. He disguised himself as an old Brahmin and asked for Vessantara's wife. Vessantara did not hesitate a moment and gave away his wife immediately.

This pleased God very much. He returned Vessantara's wife, children and kingdom.

46. The King and the Disciple

Once, a hermit and his disciples were the guests of a king. After some days, the hermit decided to go back to his hermitage. The king requested him to extend his stay. The ascetic accepted but the disciples went back.

One day, the chief disciple came back to pay homage to the hermit.

He did not notice the king standing there. The king heard him uttering, "Oh, what a great pleasure! Oh, what a great pleasure!" The king thought that the disciple was happy after eating the royal dishes, which were scarcely available in forests. He thought the disciple was greedy.

The hermit, however, read the king's mind. He told the king that the disciple was once a king himself. The words "great pleasure" were meant to show the pleasure of the life of an ascetic, which he had never experienced when he was a king. The king felt ashamed of his thoughts and apologised to the disciple.

47. The Rogue Sage

Once, a sage came to a village. A rich man gave him a place to stay.

Now, the rich man had a lot of gold. He was scared of thieves. So, he kept the gold under the sage's care.

After a few days, the sage came to the merchant and said, "I have spent enough time here. Now, I wish to leave."

The merchant bade him farewell.

The sage went some distance and came back to the merchant. He said, "I do not keep anything that belongs to others." Saying so, he took out a straw from his beard, which he himself had put there, and gave it to the merchant.

The merchant was mighty pleased with the sage's honesty. But a friend of his saw all this and grew suspicious.

He said to the merchant, "Have you checked your gold?"

They both went to check the gold. To the merchant's surprise, the gold was missing.

They caught the fraud sage. He was punished for cheating the merchant.

28

48. The Two Gamblers

Two gamblers gambled every day. One was honest but the other was a cheat. He played as long as he won. When he began to lose, he would secretly put one of the dice in his mouth and claim that it was lost. Then he would stop the game.

The honest gambler saw this happening many times. He realised that the man was a cheat. He decided to teach the cheat a lesson.

One day, he put poison on the dice and let it dry. The game started after some time.

When the cheat started losing the game, as usual, he put the dice in his mouth.

Soon he fell sick and fainted. The honest gambler, who was good at heart, cured him.

Afterwards, he advised the cheat not to deceive anyone again. Eventually, the cheat mended his ways.

49. The Clever Turtle

A king got a lake made for his children to play in with some fish in it.

The excited children rushed off to see the fish. Now, among the fish was a turtle as well. The children not having seen a turtle before thought it to be a monster.

They told the king that there was a monster in the lake. The king ordered his men to kill the monster.

There were different suggestions on how to kill it. Some said, "Crush it." Some said, "Burn it."

Finally, an old man, who had always been afraid of water said, "Throw it into the water where it will flow over the rocks and get killed."

The turtle said, "Please do not put me in the water. I will surely die!"

Hearing his pleas, the king's soldiers immediately threw the turtle in the water. The clever turtle laughed saying, "Those people do not know how safe I am in the water!"

50. The Tempting Nymph

Once there was an ascetic. He lived on the Himalayas near a lake.

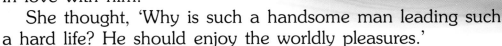

One day, he was bathing in the lake. Suddenly, a water nymph came out of the lake and saw him. She immediately fell in love with him.

She thought, 'Why is such a handsome man leading such a hard life? He should enjoy the worldly pleasures.'

She tried to impress him by singing a beautiful song. But the man remained unimpressed.

Then she went up to him and said, "Young man, why are you wasting your life in such hardships when the pleasures of the world await you. You can always become an ascetic when you are old."

The ascetic replied, "My dear lady, I can do that but who knows whether I will live to grow old or not." Hearing these words, the nymph sighed and realised that the ascetic would not be deviated and disappeared.

51. The Prince and the Monster

Once, there was a prince. He was very brave. One day, while going through the forest, he came face to face with a monster.

The monster growled, "I am going to eat you up!"

The prince said, "I will kill you with my weapons."

The prince fought very hard. The monster was surprised. He found that the prince was not afraid of him at all. He asked the prince, "Are you not afraid of me?"

The prince replied, "In my belly is my diamond weapon. It will cut you if you swallow me. So if I die, so will you! That is why I am not afraid of you."

Hearing this, the monster set him free.

In reality, the prince had no diamond in his belly. He had just made it up. His quick thinking had saved his life.

52. *The Wise Advice*

King Pratap was the ruler of a big kingdom. He had a wife and a son. One day, his kingdom was attacked by King Brij. He killed King Pratap and forcefully made the queen his own wife.

Luckily, the son (prince) escaped. When the prince grew up, he raised a large army to attack King Brij.

He sent a message to the king telling him to surrender or fight a battle.

The prince's mother heard of this. She sent a message to her son saying, "Do not fight. It would be wiser to close every entrance to the city. Lack of food and water will weaken the army. Then it will surrender immediately."

The prince followed his mother's advice. After some time, the army and the king surrendered.

The prince killed King Brij and became the new king himself. His mother was very happy.

53. *The Foolish Servant*

A king had a loyal servant. His job was to set a price for anything the king wanted to buy or sell.

But this man would buy things at very low prices and sell them at high prices.

Once, a merchant sold 500 horses. The price the servant gave was only a cup of rice for the horses.

The merchant was upset and wanted to get a good price for his horses. So, he gave the servant a valuable gift. Then, in front of the king, he asked the servant, "I want to know the actual price of one cup of rice."

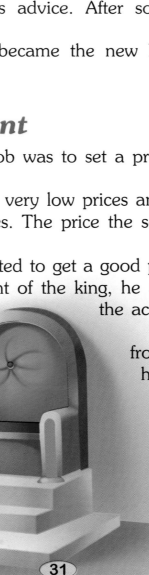

The servant, after receiving a gift from the horse dealer, wanted to please him. So he said, "One cup of rice is worth this kingdom!"

On hearing this, everyone started laughing.

The king was very embarrassed and shocked. He immediately threw the servant out of his court.

54. The Deer Who Changed the King

A king used to hunt deer. Many deer died due to this. One day, the deer king came to the king and said, "Sir! Many of my deer are dying every day. To stop this, we will send you one deer every day."

The king agreed. He was also very impressed by the deer king and said, "You will never be hunted."

So, every day one deer presented itself to the king. One day, it was the turn of a deer who had a young baby.

She went to the king and said, "O King! I want my baby to grow. Then, I will go to the king."

The deer king said, "Do not worry. I will go in your place."

The next day, the king was surprised to see the herd king.

The deer king told him everything.

The king was impressed with the deer king's sacrifice. He said, "My friend! I promise not to hunt deer anymore."

55. The Mice Which Ate the Plough

Once, two traders, Ram and Shyam, were friends. One day, Ram went on a business trip and kept his plough at Shyam's house.

Shyam sold the plough and kept the money. When Ram came back to get his plough, Shyam said, "The mice have eaten your plough." Ram was surprised at this strange answer.

That evening, Ram took Shyam's son to a friend's house saying, "Please keep this little boy here until I come back for him."

When Shyam asked Ram about his son, Ram replied, "A bird carried him away."

Shyam said, "How can a bird carry a boy?"

Shyam went to the court. The judge heard everything.

He asked Ram, "How can a bird carry a boy?"

Ram replied, "If a bird cannot carry a boy, can mice eat a plough?"

"What do you mean by that?" asked the judge.

Ram told everything.

The judge understood everything. He said to Shyam, "Give back the plough and he will give your son back."

56. Soma's Heart

Once, there was a king named Vikram. He had three friends - Nanda, Bhoj and Dhanu – and a wise minister called Soma.

Once, all friends got into a discussion and could not find a solution. Soma found a solution for them. All the friends were impressed by him.

King Nanda told his wife about Soma. She was so charmed by Soma that she wanted his heart.

Now, Nanda had a daughter. Prince Dhruva was in love with her. He asked for her hand from King Nanda.

Nanda said, "Bring me the heart of Soma and my daughter will be yours."

Dhruva went to King Vikram and challenged him to a game of dice. King Vikram lost the game and Dhruva asked for Soma as his prize.

Soma became Dhruva's slave. As soon as he was going to take his heart out, God intervened and saved him.

Dhruva was shocked. He set Soma free. In time, King Nanda and his wife also sought Soma's forgiveness.

57. The Ascetic and the Baby Elephant

A rich man became an ascetic and lived in a forest. Once, he came across a baby elephant. He instantly bonded with the baby elephant. He took it to his hermitage. From then on, he started taking care of the elephant. He fed it every day.

One day, the ascetic was away for some work. The baby elephant got hungry and ate more than it could digest. Soon, it got sick and died. When the ascetic came back, he was filled with sorrow. He remained in that state for many days.

One day, a great sage was passing by. He saw the ascetic grieving. The sage taught the ascetic not to grieve as he was a man who had given up all attachments. This sermon helped the ascetic overcome his grief and he resumed his life preaching others.

58. No Thing

Once, there was a rich man. He gave up all the riches and became a holy man. Soon, he had many followers. With the passage of time, he attained great powers.

One day, the holy man was on the verge of dying. One of his followers asked him, "Sir! What has been your greatest achievement in this life?"

The holy man, due to the shortness of breath, uttered only two words "no thing" and passed away.

But his followers were disappointed. They thought that their master had achieved nothing in life.

A great sage was passing by and heard them discussing this.

This sage was very knowledgeable. He said to the disciples, "By saying "no thing" your teacher meant that he could see beyond the ordinary things of life." In this way, the great sage explained the brilliant accomplishments of the holy man.

59. The Merchants and the Demons

Two merchants were friends. Both were going to sell their goods. They decided to travel one after the other.

The first merchant set off with his servants. On the way, they came to a place which was haunted by demons. As soon as the merchant camped there, the demons came disguised as men. They became friends with the merchant and joined his caravan. The merchant did not realise that they were demons. In the night, when the merchant and his men were sleeping, the demons ate them. Only their bones were left.

Later, the second merchant began his journey. He reached the same place where the demons lived. He found the carts, human and animal bones, and recognized that they belonged to the former caravan. The wise merchant put people on guard around the camp during the night. This time, the demons could not eat the people. The merchant finished his journey successfully.

60. The Prince and the Demon

A prince was very virtuous.

Once, while he was walking in his garden, a demon attacked and abducted the prince.

Though captured, the prince was not afraid of the demon.

The demon was surprised to see this. He asked the prince, "Are you not afraid of me?"

The prince replied, "No. I am ready for death."

The demon was very impressed by the prince. He said to the prince, "Ask me for a boon for I am pleased with you."

The prince replied, "What can you grant me? You yourself are bound by passion and evil deeds. So how can you favour me?"

The demon was moved by the prince's words. He felt ashamed of himself. He vowed to lead a good life. He freed all his prisoners and the prince.

From then onwards, the demon became a follower of the prince.

61. The Kind Minister

A king had a wise minister who understood the language of animals.

One day, while walking on the beach, he saw a big fish with his pretty wife.

The male fish was so enchanted by his wife that he did not see some fishermen casting a net on him. Alas! He was caught.

The minister heard what the male fish was saying. He was saying, "My wife! My wife! I must be with my wife! I care for her much more than for my life!"

The minister felt sorry for the fish. He went to the fishermen and said, "Can I buy a fish from you?"

One fisherman replied, "Sir, please accept a fish from us as a gift instead!"

The minister chose the big male fish and released it in the sea. The fish thanked the minister for his kindness.

62. Justice is Served

Once there were two merchants, Baku and Raku. They were very good friends. One day, Raku lost all his wealth and became poor. He came to Baku for help. Baku was very kind and generous. He immediately gave away half of his wealth to Raku. The grateful Raku promised to help Baku whenever he needed his help.

Several years later, Baku became poor. He remembered Raku and came to him for help.

But Raku had changed and refused to help him.

Baku became sad and was very disappointed. Now, Baku's servant heard everything. He immediately went to the king and presented Baku's case to him.

The king heard everything. He immediately ordered that Raku should share half of his wealth with Baku. Thus, justice was served as Baku too had given half his share to Raku when he had lost his wealth.

63. The Brahmin Who Lied

A low-caste learned man taught a Brahmin a magic spell through which he could obtain mangoes even when they were out of season.

The Brahmin amassed great wealth by using this magic. His name spread far and wide.

The king heard about him and asked him, "From where do you get such a lovely fruit when it is not in the season?"

The Brahmin replied, "It is through a magical spell."

The king asked him, "Who taught you this great magic spell?"

The Brahmin was embarrassed to say that he had learnt it from a man of low caste, so he lied, "It was a world-renowned teacher who taught me." But as soon as he lied, he lost his magic.

The Brahmin realised his mistake. He went to the teacher and told him everything. He begged his forgiveness. But the teacher did not forgive him and the Brahmin lost the magic forever.

64. The Sea-Goddess and the Sack of Gold

Once, two brothers earned a lot of wealth. They were returning home via the sea. The younger of the two was greedy. He looked at a sack of gold which belonged to his brother. He replaced the gold sack with a sand sack. After that he threw the sand sack into the water. But, that sack was the gold sack.

The younger brother lied to his elder brother that his gold sack had fallen into the river by mistake.

The sea-goddess saw all this. She became a fish and swallowed the gold sack.

The fish was put up for sale. The person who bought the fish was none other than the elder brother.

As soon as his wife cut the fish, she found gold inside.

Then, the sea-goddess appeared and told them everything. When confronted, the greedy brother apologised for his misdeeds. The elder brother forgave him immediately.

65. The Traders and the Demon

A father and a son were traders. One day, during their travels, they took a rest in a deserted house. A man warned them that it was a haunted house.

The demon who haunted the house had received a boon from a certain king. The boon was–if any man who entered it should sneeze, the other should wish him long life. The blessed man, on the other hand, should wish the same to the other.

During the night, the father sneezed. The son did not wish him long life. The demon got ready to eat him. But the son saw the demon and immediately wished his father long life.

The demon thought, 'I cannot eat him now but I shall eat his father, for he has not wished him back.'

But the father immediately guessed everything and said to his son, "Long life to you, too!"

The demon was disappointed as he could not eat any of them.

66. The Promise

Long ago, there was a king. He was known all over for his kind heart. One day, he was taking a round of his kingdom.

While on his round, he came upon a couple. The couple was very sad.

The king asked the couple, "Why are you so sad?"

The couple told him, "We are sad because we do not have any child."

The king felt very sad for the couple. He went to his palace, took his son and gave him to the couple.

The couple was very happy to have the child. He promised the couple that he would never ask for his child.

After some time, the king started missing his child. He grew sad. His minister saw this and organised a sword show for him.

In the show, a man swallowed swords. The king asked his minister, "Is there anything more difficult than swallowing swords."

The minister replied, "Keeping a promise without regretting it is far more difficult."

The king understood what the minister meant.

67. The Honest Man

Once, there was a sacred tree. A holy spirit resided in that tree. Many people came to pray to the spirit and offered precious gifts to it. One day, a poor man brought a loaf of bread to offer to the spirit. But he did not offer it as he felt the spirit would not accept such a lowly gift. He turned to go back, but as he did so, the spirit appeared before the man. It said, "Where are you going? Give me the bread. I am hungry." The man was tongue-tied and gave it the bread. The spirit ate the bread. Then it told the man, "A pot of gold is buried here. Dig it and take it." But the poor man did no such thing. He was very honest and told the king about it. The king was pleased with the poor man's honesty and made him his royal treasurer.

68. *As You Sow, So Shall You Reap*

Once, there was a man who had a beautiful wife. He loved his wife very much. But the wife was very cruel. She ill-treated her in-laws who were blind.

One day, she said to her husband, "Leave your parents in the forest. I cannot take care of them."

At first, the man refused but due to constant nagging of his wife, he agreed.

So, one day, he took his old blind parents into the forest. As he was leaving them there, his parents begged, "Please do not leave us here as we are blind."

But the man did not listen and went away. On the way, he fell into a deep pit. He hurt his legs. A sage, who was passing by, took him out of the pit.

But the damage had been done. The man became a cripple.

He realised that since he had mistreated his parents, he had been punished. He went back and sought his parents' forgiveness.

69. *The Greedy Salesman*

Once, a salesman sold pots and pans and trinkets. A girl wanted to buy a bracelet from him but she had no money. She asked her grandmother, "Can we give our dirty old plate in exchange for the bracelet?" The grandmother agreed.

The salesman examined the plate and realised that it was of gold. But he didn't tell them so. Instead, he said, "This plate has no value." He went away. In fact, he wanted to take the plate free of cost at a later time.

Meanwhile, another salesman came there. Again, the girl wanted a bracelet. The grandmother showed the plate to the salesman.

The salesman said to the grandmother, "This plate is of gold!"

The grandmother was shocked. The salesman took the gold plate, and in exchange, gave away all his pots, pans and trinkets.

After some time, the greedy salesman returned. He asked for the plate. The grandmother was very angry and called him a liar. The greedy salesman ran away.

70. The Clever Antelope

Once, an antelope lived in a forest. It had a favourite tree whose fruits it used to eat every day. A hunter also used to hunt in that same area. One day, the hunter saw the antelope eating fruits from his favourite tree. After that, the hunter observed the antelope for a few more days. He guessed that unlike the other animals, this antelope ate fruits from that tree only. He decided to trap the antelope. He laid out some fruits under the tree, placed his trap under it, and waited for the antelope. The antelope came to the tree as usual but it was surprised to find so many fruits scattered around. Suddenly, it saw the trap and understood everything. It also realised that the hunter was near by. So, it exclaimed, "My tree is behaving strangely today so I will go to another tree today." Saying so, it ran away.

71. The Minister and the Goat's Dry Dung

A king had a very talkative minister. Once he started talking no one could say a word. The king was fed up of him and wanted to teach him a lesson.

Now, there was a man who was a wonderful marksman. The king came to know about him. He went to the man and said, "I have a very talkative minister. Do you think you could stop his talking?"

The man replied, "Yes, I can."

The next day, the marksman stood behind a curtain with a pea-shooter full of a goat's dry dung. Soon, the minister came to the king and started talking. Quickly, the marksman shot the pellets of the goat's dung. The minister swallowed down the pellets.

The king remarked to the minister, "You were so busy talking that you swallowed the goat's dung."

The minister was too embarrassed to say anything. After that, he never opened his mouth to speak.

The king rewarded the marksman generously.

72. The Price of Disobedience

Once, a merchant and his wife were very religious. They had a son who never prayed or performed any religious duties. One day, his mother sent him to a temple to listen to a saint's sermons. She hoped that listening to the sermons would change him. She also promised to give him money if he went there. The son, of course, went to the temple, but he slept throughout the sermon.

The next day, when the son came back home, his mother gave him the money as she had promised. She thought her son would invite the saint to their house, but he did no such thing.

Instead, after getting the money, he decided to go abroad for business. His mother pleaded with him not to go but he went off.

But, as his ship was in the midst of the sea, a violent storm shook the sea. The ship sank and so did the son. Thus, he paid the price of not listening to his mother.

73. The Great Ascetic

Once, a baby was born in a family of Brahmins. This baby was very illustrious. The baby turned into a very educated man in time.

One day, he renounced the world and became an ascetic. He performed heavy penances.

The stories of his penances and dedication spread everywhere. God also heard about them. He wanted to test the ascetic.

He tested the ascetic in many ways. There were times when the ascetic was left with nothing to eat as God used to disguise himself and beg for alms. The ascetic would give away whatever food he had.

But despite the hardships, the ascetic remained calm.

Finally, after putting the ascetic through many hardships, God appeared before him.

He said to the ascetic, "Ask me for any boon."

The ascetic said, "Please bless me so that I may not sway from my path."

God was very pleased and blessed him, and disappeared.

74. The Righteous Minister

A king had a minister. He was very judicious. The king also had a lawyer who used to take bribes and give wrong decisions in court cases. One day, as usual, he took bribe and gave a wrong decision. The accused came to the minister for help.

The minister looked at the case. He fought the case and won it. The people praised him and the king made him the judge.

However, the lawyer was very angry. He became jealous of the minister and wanted to put him in trouble.

One day, he told the king that the minister was getting more popular than the king.

The king became insecure and gave the minister various impossible tasks to perform. The minister, with the help of God, performed all of them.

The king was very impressed. He realised that the lawyer was jealous of the minister and was extracting revenge. He banished the lawyer from his kingdom.

75. The Clever Prince

Once, the king of Banaras fought and conquered another kingdom. He took all the wealth of that kingdom to his own kingdom. He filled the wealth in iron pots and buried the pots in the royal garden.

Now, unknown to him, the prince of that kingdom escaped in disguise. Later, he became an ascetic and reached Banaras with his disciples.

The king was charmed by the ascetic's wisdom and made him a royal guest.

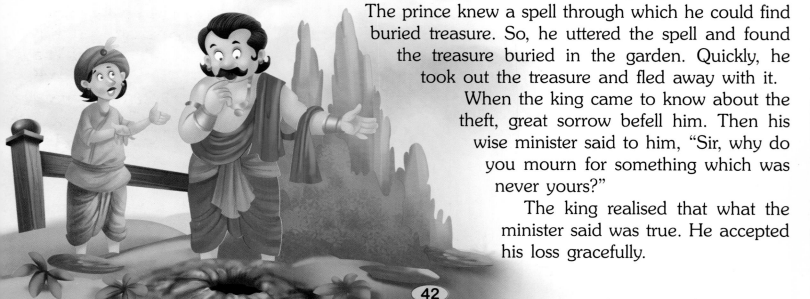

The prince knew a spell through which he could find buried treasure. So, he uttered the spell and found the treasure buried in the garden. Quickly, he took out the treasure and fled away with it.

When the king came to know about the theft, great sorrow befell him. Then his wise minister said to him, "Sir, why do you mourn for something which was never yours?"

The king realised that what the minister said was true. He accepted his loss gracefully.

76. The Naga King

Once, there was a prince named Gautam. When he came of age, he became the king and his father renounced the world and became an ascetic.

He lived in a forest on the bank of a river. The river was named after a Naga king. The Naga king was very kind and compassionate. He was also very religious. He was greatly impressed by the ascetic. Soon, they became good friends. One day, King Gautam visited the hermitage. There, he met the Naga king and was impressed by him.

One day, some men seized the Naga king. They wanted to steal the gem on his head. But King Gautam came to the rescue of the Naga king. He fought with the men and freed the Naga king.

The Naga king thanked King Gautam for saving his life.

77. The Fire-God and the Quail

Once, a quail lived in a nest with its siblings. Now, this quail was different from its siblings. Unlike the other quails, it never ate worms or insects. It relied only on twigs. As a result, it became weak. One day, while the other quails were away looking for food, a fierce fire broke out in the jungle. One by one, all the animals ran from the forest but the quail could not fly as it was very weak. Slowly, the fire closed in on the quail's nest. The quail said to the fire-god, "O Lord! I am too weak to fly. All my brothers are away. I can offer you nothing but my weak body." Hearing the quail's emotional words, the fire-god took pity on it and retreated without harming the nest.

78. The True Friend

Once, a barber and a scholar were friends. They travelled a lot. One day, while travelling, their ship sank. The two floated on a wooden plank and reached an island. On the island, the barber hunted a wild animal and roasted it. He offered the roasted meat to the scholar but the scholar refused. Instead, he sat down and meditated.

Impressed with his devotion, the sea spirit came out of the sea. It offered to take the scholar ashore on a huge ship full of precious stones. The scholar agreed but he wanted the spirit to take his friend as well.

The spirit refused saying the barber had not led a pious life and had committed many sins.

The scholar thought for a moment and then said to the spirit, "Give the benefits of my piety to my friend and take him ashore."

The sea spirit was surprised and happy to see the scholar's sacrifice. It agreed to take them both. Later, both became very rich.

79. The King's Royal Guests

Long ago, a sage and his disciples lived high in the mountains. Once, it rained a lot. The disciples decided to go to the nearest village and seek alms. The sage sat deep in meditation while the disciples left. Upon reaching the village, they started seeking alms. Now, the king of that province was on a visit there. He saw the disciples and invited them to his palace. The disciples became the king's royal guests. They had plenty to eat and drink.

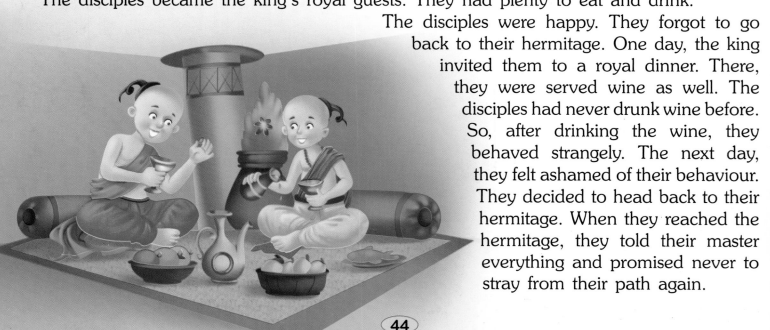

The disciples were happy. They forgot to go back to their hermitage. One day, the king invited them to a royal dinner. There, they were served wine as well. The disciples had never drunk wine before. So, after drinking the wine, they behaved strangely. The next day, they felt ashamed of their behaviour. They decided to head back to their hermitage. When they reached the hermitage, they told their master everything and promised never to stray from their path again.

80. The Spell

A priest knew a special magic spell which could be used only once a year, when the planets were lined up in a certain way. Then he had only to clap his hands, and a shower of precious gems came down on him.

One day, the priest and his student were travelling when they were captured by some robbers.

They said, "We will release you only when you give us 500 gold coins."

The student whispered to the priest, "Sir, it is that time of the year when your magic spell will work. The planets will be lined in a special way tonight."

The priest said to the robbers, "I will give you the coins but you will have to wait till night falls."

The robbers agreed. During night time, the priest uttered the spell and was covered with precious gems.

The excited robbers got greedy. They started fighting among themselves. In the meanwhile, the priest and the student took all the gems and ran away.

81. Friends in Need

Long ago, there lived a family of hawks on a tree in a forest. They made friends with a lion, a kingfisher and a turtle.

One day, some hunters came to the forest. They saw the baby hawks and wanted to eat them. They burnt a huge fire for the same.

The mother hawk saw this. She told her husband, "Call our friends for help or these hunters will eat our babies."

The father hawk flew away to call his friends. The kingfisher, the tiger and the turtle arrived immediately. The kingfisher saw the burning fire and sprinkled water on the fire with its beak. Then, the turtle put sand on the fire and put it out.

After that the lion roared loudly. The hunters got scared of the lion and ran away. The hawks thanked their friends for their timely help. All of them lived happily after that.

82. The Just King

A king and a queen had a son. He was very intelligent. He succeeded his father as a king when he grew up. He proved to be a very able ruler. His name spread far and wide. Even the gods heard about him. Now, when the rain-god heard about him, he got jealous. He thought, 'How could a mere mortal become so powerful? I will teach him a lesson. Let me see how he saves his people from me.' The rain-god stopped sending

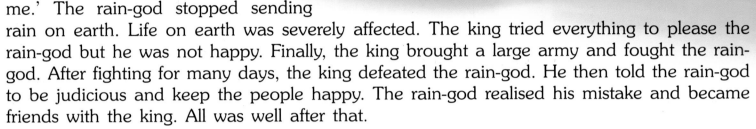

rain on earth. Life on earth was severely affected. The king tried everything to please the rain-god but he was not happy. Finally, the king brought a large army and fought the rain-god. After fighting for many days, the king defeated the rain-god. He then told the rain-god to be judicious and keep the people happy. The rain-god realised his mistake and became friends with the king. All was well after that.

83. The King's Advisors

A king had five advisors. But these advisors gave wrong advice to the king for their personal gains. One day, a learned Brahmin came to the king's court. At that time, the advisors were discussing a case. The Brahmin quickly solved the case. The king was very impressed by him and kept him as his advisor. The other advisors of the king became jealous of the Brahmin. Slowly, they started poisoning the king's ears against the Brahmin till the king had been completely brainwashed.

From then, the king ignored the advice of the Brahmin. The Brahmin realised something was wrong.

One day, he overheard the advisors talking. One said, "Look, how we took care of the Brahmin. The king does not pay heed to his advice at all."

While they conversed, the Brahmin quickly brought the king there and made him hear their conversation.

The king was shocked and immediately punished his advisors. Later, he apologised to the Brahmin.

84. The Monk

Once, there were two brothers. They were monks.

Now, while the elder brother was very intelligent, the younger one was dim-witted. The elder brother could memorise everything their master taught but the younger one could not.

One day, the elder brother, noting his brother's inability to learn, told him, "It is better for you to do some other work as you cannot learn these difficult verses."

The younger brother agreed and left the monastery. On the way, he met a learned sage. The sage understood everything by looking at the younger brother.

He told the younger brother, "Even if you cannot learn the verses, you can stand outside the monastery with a rug and help the monks clean their feet."

The younger brother was very happy and did as advised. When his elder brother saw him doing this, he was very happy. He took him back into the monastery. From then on, the younger brother went on doing charity and became a great monk.

85. The Wise Disciple

Long ago, in a jungle, there lived a stag. The stag was very wise and the leader of his herd. In that herd, was the wise stag's nephew as well. The wise stag taught the nephew all that was needed to survive in the jungle. The nephew was a good learner and followed his uncle's advice.

One day, when the herd was grazing, the nephew felt thirsty. He saw a river at a distance and headed towards it. Unknowing to him, a hunter had laid a trap there.

And lo! The nephew was caught in the trap. He shouted for help but the herd was far away. No one heard him. At first, the nephew got frightened. Then, slowly, he calmed himself and started thinking. He remembered the teachings of his uncle to survive in a jungle.

Immediately, he pretended to be dead, for he remembered that a hunter never took a dead animal.

As expected, the hunter did not take the stag. Thus, the stag was saved.

86. The Greedy Servants

There was a rich wise merchant. Once, he set off with his servants and carts of goods to sell them.

After travelling a great distance, they reached a forest. The merchant had heard a lot about this forest. He called his servants and warned them, "Do not eat anything of this jungle as a demon has sprinkled poison over them."

A demon had seen them. He put honey on some leaves and sprinkled it with poison.

The merchant, in the meanwhile, went to get some water. While he was away, some servants of the merchant felt hungry. They could not resist the honey. They immediately ate the honey and died within minutes. Soon, the demon came and ate them.

The merchant came back and saw the bones. He felt sad for the servants and said, "Oh! If only they had not been so greedy!"

87. Bodhisattva and the Monster

The Bodhisattva was once born as an ascetic. A monster used to come to listen to the Bodhisattva's teachings but never followed them.

One day, a beautiful lady was going to her parents' house through the forest.

The monster liked her and locked her in a box, fearing she might run away. He would swallow the box whenever he went out.

One day, the monster was passing by the river. He spat out the box and went to bathe in the river, leaving the box on the shore. The lady somehow managed to get out of the box.

She saw a young man who had a magic sword. Wanting to get rid of the monster, the lady hid the young man's sword in the box with herself.

The monster came out of the river. He swallowed the box again and went to listen to the Bodhisattva's teachings. Just as the Bodhisattva saw the monster, he warned him that his life was in danger.

The monster spat out the box immediately and his life was saved. Then, the monster let the lady free at the Bodhisattva's advice.

88. The Kind Deed

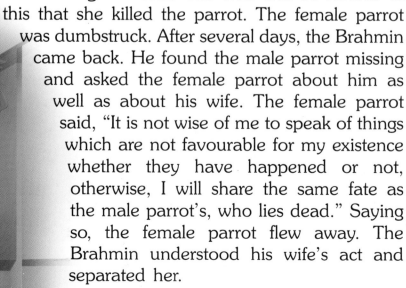

A king loved his wife very much. He loved her to the extent of being jealous and possessive about her.

After a few years, the queen bore a son. The son had a god-like beauty about him.

The queen loved her son and spent most of her time with him. The king realised this. He started getting jealous of his son.

One day, as the king came to meet her, the queen was playing with her son. She did not notice the king. The king was offended by this.

He thought, 'If this goes on, she will ignore me forever. I will have to do something.'

So he called the executioner. He told him to kill his son. The queen pleaded with the king but he did not listen. The executioner took the child but could not kill him. He left him in a hermitage. He, then, brought the queen there. The queen was very happy and lived with her son in the hermitage.

89. The Brahmin and the Parrot

Once, a Brahmin had two parrots – a male and a female. The Brahmin took great care of them. But the Brahmin's wife was very wicked and immoral. One day, the Brahmin had to go out of town. He told the parrots to keep an eye on his wife. Now, as soon as the Brahmin went away, men started visiting the Brahmin's wife. The male parrot scolded the wife for being immoral. The wife was so furious at this that she killed the parrot. The female parrot was dumbstruck. After several days, the Brahmin came back. He found the male parrot missing and asked the female parrot about him as well as about his wife. The female parrot said, "It is not wise of me to speak of things which are not favourable for my existence whether they have happened or not, otherwise, I will share the same fate as the male parrot's, who lies dead." Saying so, the female parrot flew away. The Brahmin understood his wife's act and separated her.

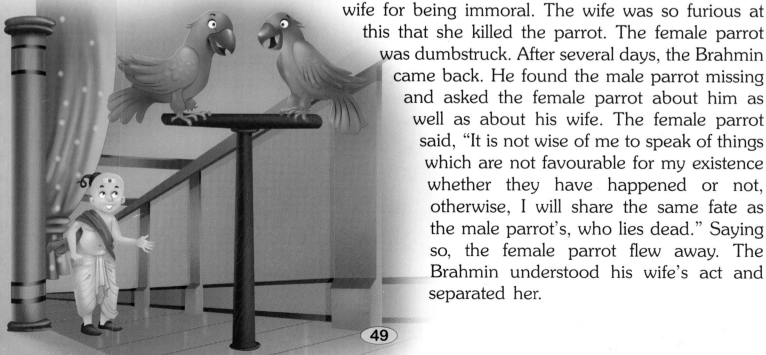

90. The Frog's Advice

Once, fishermen set traps for fish in rivers. One day, in a certain river, many fish got caught in a trap. A snake, seeing the fish trapped in the net, went into the trap himself with the aim of eating the fish. But he was in for a surprise as the fish got united and bit him everywhere. The snake was deeply wounded. He immediately freed himself from the trap. Now, a frog had observed everything.

The snake seeing the frog observing everything looked at him and asked, "Did you see the behaviour of the fish? Was it justified?"

The frog answered, "Yes, it was justified. If you eat the fish when they enter your domain, will the fish not eat you if you entered theirs? Everyone is powerful in his own field."

The snake accepted the answer and quietly went away.

91. The King Who Changed His Ways

A king was famous for his wickedness. He tortured his people and used power to control them. The people of his kingdom were very unhappy. One day, as he lay fast asleep, a

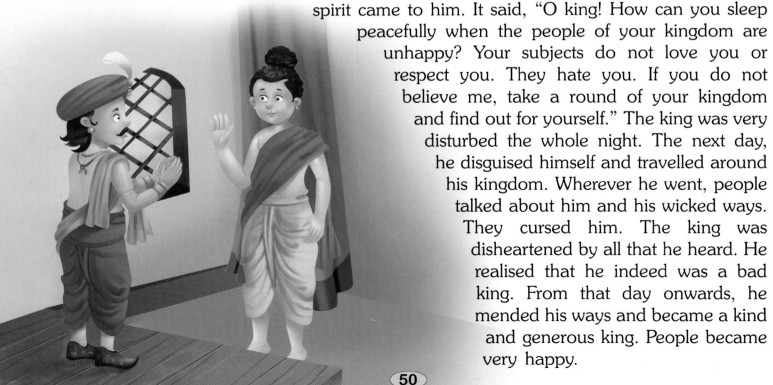

spirit came to him. It said, "O king! How can you sleep peacefully when the people of your kingdom are unhappy? Your subjects do not love you or respect you. They hate you. If you do not believe me, take a round of your kingdom and find out for yourself." The king was very disturbed the whole night. The next day, he disguised himself and travelled around his kingdom. Wherever he went, people talked about him and his wicked ways. They cursed him. The king was disheartened by all that he heard. He realised that he indeed was a bad king. From that day onwards, he mended his ways and became a kind and generous king. People became very happy.

92. The Minister and the King

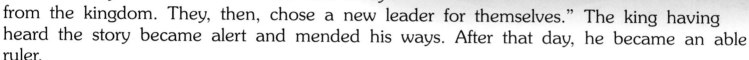

Once, a king was very lazy. He never worked and spent his entire time resting and sleeping. He never looked into the welfare of the people. The people of his kingdom grew restless because of this. Now, the king had a wise minister. He knew that it would be useless to tell the king to work. So, he thought of a different way to motivate the king. He said to the king, "Sir, there was once a tortoise king. He was very lazy and never worked for the betterment of his people. The people were so angry with him that they beat him and drove him away from the kingdom. They, then, chose a new leader for themselves." The king having heard the story became alert and mended his ways. After that day, he became an able ruler.

93. The King's Dream

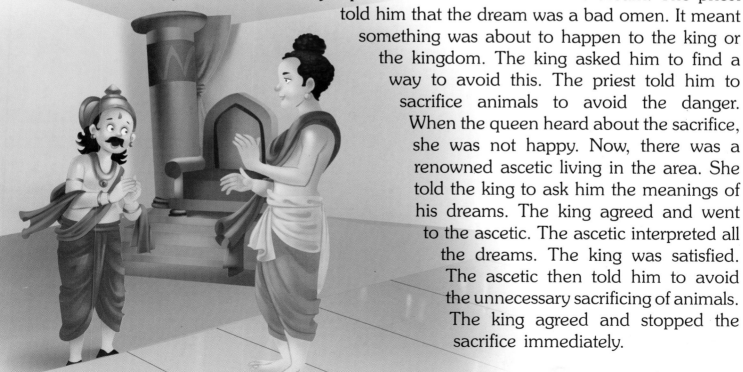

Once, a king saw some terrible dream. He was very upset after this and could not sleep. The next day, he called his royal priest and told him about his dream. The priest told him that the dream was a bad omen. It meant something was about to happen to the king or the kingdom. The king asked him to find a way to avoid this. The priest told him to sacrifice animals to avoid the danger. When the queen heard about the sacrifice, she was not happy. Now, there was a renowned ascetic living in the area. She told the king to ask him the meanings of his dreams. The king agreed and went to the ascetic. The ascetic interpreted all the dreams. The king was satisfied. The ascetic then told him to avoid the unnecessary sacrificing of animals. The king agreed and stopped the sacrifice immediately.

94. The Merchant and His Son

Long ago, there lived a rich merchant. He was very wise and honest. One day, he died and left all he had earned for his son. The rich merchant, due to his kind deeds, became a divine being in heaven. Now, the son was a scoundrel. He squandered away all the wealth in gambling and other bad activities and became poor. The merchant saw all this and felt pity for his son. So, he appeared in front of his son, and said, "Take this wishing cup and wish for anything and it will appear. Also, I advise you to mend your ways." The son took the cup and became rich. But he did not mend his ways. One day, in a drunken state, he broke the cup and became poor again. The merchant could only sigh from above.

95. The Elephants Who Did Not Trample

Once, there lived a wise man in a village of just thirty families. The wise man taught all that was good and noble. As a result, the village became crime-free.

However, the village headman was unhappy. Earlier, when crimes occurred, he used to punish people, collect fines, etc. But it was all over now. So, to gain back all that, he went to the king and said, "Some villages are being robbed by thieves."

The king ordered, "Catch them and have them trampled by elephants."

The headman falsely accused the heads of the thirty families and the wise man as the thieves. Later, when they were laid to be trampled, the elephants refused to trample them.

The king was surprised. The wise man said, "We have done no wrong. Our minds are pure and harmless. This purity was seen by the elephants, so they did not harm us."

Then, the wise man told the king everything. The king punished the headman.

96. The Ugly Prince

A king had no son though he had sixteen thousand queens. Seeing his pain, one of the queens performed severe penances. God granted her two sons – one wise but ugly and the other foolish but handsome.

When the ugly prince came of age, his parents thought of marrying him off. They found a very beautiful princess for him. But they knew that no wise woman would marry their ugly son. So, they told the princess that she could only see her husband after she had a child.

One day, the princess insisted on seeing her husband. The queen showed her the younger son. The princess was happy to have such a handsome prince as her husband.

But, one day, as she was walking in the garden, the elder prince came up to her and said, "I am your husband." The princess was shocked and furious, for she had been tricked. She went back to her father. But the wise elder prince won her heart through his wisdom.

97. The Sweet Figs

A kingdom was ruled by a very just and kind king. One day, the king went around his kingdom in disguise to see how the people were faring under his rule. While moving around, he came to a hermitage. An ascetic saw him and offered him some figs. The king found the figs very sweet in taste. The ascetic replied, "The fruits are sweet because the king is a wise ruler." The king was surprised by this answer, so he asked the ascetic, "What if the king was unjust? Would the figs lose their sweetness?"

The ascetic replied, "Yes, if the king is unjust not only the figs but also the whole atmosphere loses its sweetness."

The king returned to his palace. To test the ascetic's words, he started ruling his kingdom unjustly. After some days, he again went to the ascetic and tasted the figs. This time the figs were bitter. The king decided to rule justly and make the figs sweet again.

98. The Rat, the Parrot, the Snake and the Sage

Once, a wicked prince was swept away by a storm. A rat, a snake and a parrot were also swept away. They found a log and climbed on it.

A sage saw that and saved them. He comforted the the rat, the parrot and the snake first and then came to the prince. The prince did not like the second treatment.

Later, the rat, the parrot and the snake said to the sage, "Whenever you need money, we will help you."

The prince also said, "When I will be the king, I will give you great riches."

After many years, the sage wanted to test all those whom he had saved. True to their word, the rat, the parrot and the snake gave him great riches. But the prince, who had become a king, did not. Instead, he ordered the sage to be killed. When the sage told the people his story, they killed the king and made the sage the king. He invited the rat, the parrot and the snake to live in the palace forever.

99. The Naga Serpent

There were two kings. One was very kind and the other was very cruel. The kind king's kingdom flourished partly due to his kindness and partly due to the presence of a Naga serpent. The cruel king's kingdom did not prosper at all. As a result, people starting leaving their kingdom and went to the kind king's kingdom. The cruel king came to know about this. As a result, he mended his ways and wanted to bring the Naga serpent to his kingdom for prosperity. He hired a snake charmer for the task. The Naga serpent came to know of the snake charmer. He approached a hunter to kill the snake charmer. The hunter killed the snake charmer and was rewarded handsomely by the Naga serpent. The Naga serpent continued to stay in the kind king's kingdom.

100. God Tests the Ascetics

Once, there were eight siblings. The eldest, a boy, mastered all the religious books and teachings. He became very famous for his profound knowledge. He renounced the world and became an ascetic. His siblings followed his footsteps. They started dwelling in a forest.

The ascetics used to eat lotus stalks for food. They became renowned for their penance and meditation. God, too, heard about them and wanted to test them.

So, one day, when their food had been laid out, God stole the food kept for the eldest ascetic. The eldest ascetic, seeing his food missing, went away without saying anything. This kept happening for four days consecutively, but still the eldest ascetic did not utter a word.

On the fifth day, the other ascetics noticed that the eldest ascetic had become very weak. They came to know of the reason. Instead of talking ill of the thief, they only prayed for his prosperity. God felt happy to see the attitude of all ascetics and blessed them.

101. The Bitter Leaf

An ascetic was a royal guest of a king. He stayed in the royal park and spent time in meditation. Now the king had a son. The son was ill-tempered. The king had called many

teachers to reform his son but they had all given up. The king requested the ascetic to help him. One day, when the ascetic was walking in the garden with the son, he pointed to a leaf of a plant and told the son to taste it. As soon as the son bit the leaf, he threw it out, as it was bitter. The ascetic pointed out, "If there is so much bitterness in a baby plant, how much bitterness will there be when it grows up?" The son understood the meaning of the ascetic's words and changed himself from that day. The king was very happy and thanked the ascetic for his help.

102. The Test

Long ago, a learned Brahmin had a son. The Brahmin sent his son to a hermitage for education. One day, the teacher decided to test the students. He told them, "I am very poor. I need money. The best way to get money is to steal it." All the students, except the Brahmin's son, started planning various ways of stealing money. The teacher noticed that all the students were busy except for the Brahmin's son. The teacher came to him and asked, "Why are you sitting here? Are you not going to steal for me? Do you not have pity for me?" The student replied, "Sir, I sympathise with you fully. I can do anything for you except stealing. It is against my principles." The teacher was very happy as the student had passed his test. The teacher said, "You have passed my test with flying colours. You are truly virtuous."

103. The Fine Leather Straps

Once, a king was out in his chariot. His chariot was drawn by two white horses with fine leather straps. When he came back, nobody bothered to unfasten the fine leather straps. The king's royal dogs chewed on the leather straps. The next day, a servant told the king that some stray dogs had chewed the fine leather straps. The king was very angry and gave death sentence to all the stray dogs. The dogs went to their king for help.

The king of dogs was a divine spirit. He went to the king and spoke in a human voice, "I will prove to you that the royal dogs ate the leather straps and not the stray dogs."

He requested a servant to bring buttermilk and grass for all the royal dogs. As soon as the dogs drank the milk, they vomited. With the vomit, came out bits of leather." The king was satisfied and took back the death sentence.

104. The Dog and His Debt

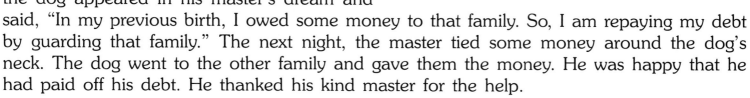

A dog was very loyal to his master. His master was also very happy with him. But, his master noticed that his dog went away somewhere in the night and came back in the morning all wet. The master decided to follow his dog one night. He discovered that his dog swam across a river and guarded another family at night. The master got very angry with his dog. That night, the dog appeared in his master's dream and said, "In my previous birth, I owed some money to that family. So, I am repaying my debt by guarding that family." The next night, the master tied some money around the dog's neck. The dog went to the other family and gave them the money. He was happy that he had paid off his debt. He thanked his kind master for the help.

105. The Dumb Prince

Once, a queen was childless. She prayed for a child and her wish got fulfilled. Once, the prince heard his father giving a harsh punishment to some men. The prince was disturbed, as he did not want to punish anyone. He decided never to become a king. But, he needed a way to avoid being a king. A priest advised him to become dumb and inactive to avoid being made the king. The prince did likewise. The king realised that his son would never become well and decided to end his suffering. He told his servant to kill him. When the servant was preparing to kill him, the prince got up and told the servant everything. Then he went and told his parents why he had become dumb and inactive. He took their blessings and became an ascetic. Later, his parents also followed him.

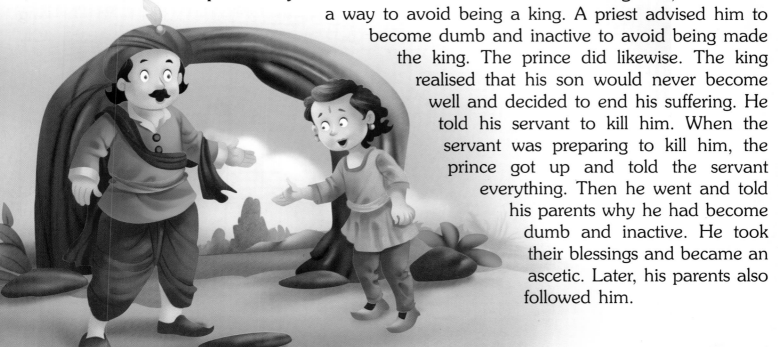

106. The Tortoise and His Home

Once, a river was full of many sea creatures. Sometimes, the river used to be dry and sometimes the river used to be full of water. Now, the sea creatures knew by instinct when there would be drought and when there would be rainfall.

Now, there came a time when there was going to be drought. So, the sea creatures left the river and went away to greener pastures. But a tortoise did not leave the river. He said, "I was born here and my parents also lived here, so I cannot leave this river."

When the river dried up, the tortoise buried himself in the clay. Just then, a potter came to take some clay. His spade hit the tortoise. The tortoise cried, "Ouch! I made a mistake in staying here. This is not a safe place anymore. It is useless to cling to things. One should move on in life." Saying so, he ran away as fast as he could.

107. The Wise Beggar Woman

Once, there was a king and a queen. One day, they yet saw a beggar woman at the palace gates. Though the beggar woman was in a poor state yet she had a contented smile on her face. The queen noticed this smile and was attracted to the beggar woman. She took some food for the beggar woman and gave it to her. As the woman started eating, the queen asked her, "Though you are a beggar yet you have smile on your face. Why?"

The woman replied, "I smile because I feel lucky to be alive." The queen was impressed with the woman's wisdom. After that she met the woman every day. One day, the king saw her talking to the beggar woman. Later, he asked the queen why she was spending so much time with a beggar. The queen did not say anything but took him to meet her. The king, too, was impressed with the woman's wisdom. Both became good friends of the beggar woman.

108. A Mother's Pain

A mother placed her baby on a mat and bathed in the river.

A demon wanted to eat the baby. He disguised himself as a woman and asked the mother, "Can I take your baby for a stroll?" The mother agreed.

But after some time, the mother saw the woman running. She ran after the woman and asked, "Where are you taking my baby?"

The woman replied, "This baby is mine, not yours!"

A saint heard them and asked what the matter was. After hearing everything, he told the demon to hold the baby's arms, and the mother, to hold its legs. He told both of them to pull the baby towards themselves.

But, the mother, seeing how her baby cried, freed him.

The sage said, "This baby belongs to the woman who freed the baby because she could not bear to see the baby crying whereas the other woman had no emotions or pity for the baby."

The mother thanked the sage while the demon ran away.

109. The Afterlife

An ascetic because of his good deeds dwelled in heaven. But despite living in heaven and enjoying the bliss, he loved to erase the sufferings of the earthly people. One day, while he was looking at the earth, he saw a king who held the belief that there was no afterlife. With this belief in mind, he became immoral and greedy. The ascetic decided to change the king's ways. He appeared before the king. The king was surprised to see him. He never thought that divine beings existed. The ascetic gave him sermons on right conduct and afterlife. The king understood that there was life after death. People were punished for their wrong actions or rewarded for their good actions in the after world. He promised the ascetic to reform his ways and follow the right path.

110. The Ascetic Who Tortured Himself

Once, an ascetic heard that the holiest people were those who endured sufferings and tortured their bodies. The ascetic decided to test this theory. Thus, he went to live in the darkest of the forests to be away from any human contact. He ate dirt and ashes. In the summer season, he spent his days under the trees, thereby, being burnt by the bright rays of the sun. During the winter season, he got covered with snow. Thus, he tortured his body throughout the different seasons. This was how he passed his life.

Then, one day, he had a vision in which he saw himself in hell. The ascetic realised that despite going through such severities, he would still go to hell. Therefore, after that, he gave up torturing himself.

111. The Tree Spirit

Once, a king wished for a palace supported on only one column unlike the other palaces that were supported by many columns. The builders spotted a strong sal tree in the royal garden whose trunk could be used as a column. But this tree was a sacred tree and worshipped by people. A spirit lived in the tree. The spirit thought, 'If they cut my tree, the other trees will also be harmed.' It went to the king and said, "I have lived on this tree for many years. Now, it is to be cut but I request you to cut it in such a way that the other trees will not be harmed if it falls." The king was taken aback by this humble request. He realised that the tree spirit was ready to sacrifice its tree but did not want any harm to the other trees. He, therefore, cancelled the idea of a new palace.

112. The Wild Elephant

Once an ascetic found a baby elephant and reared it as his own. The elephant started growing up over the years. The other ascetics were scared of keeping a wild elephant in their premises. The ascetic's teacher advised him, "As long as the elephant was a baby, it was okay to keep it in the hermitage. But now that it has grown up, it is dangerous to keep the elephant here. It may lose its temper and become wild at any moment." The ascetic did not pay heed to his teacher's advice. He thought, 'I have reared the elephant as my own baby. It will never harm me.' Now, one day, all the ascetics left the hermitage to perform a ceremony except the one who raised the elephant.

Suddenly, the elephant lost its temper and started trampling everything that got in its way. The elephant did not spare its master as well. When the teacher returned, he said, "If only he would have listened to me."

113. The Man Who Read Footprints

A man once had special powers. He could read footprints. The king was impressed with his powers and made him his minister. One day, the king himself committed a crime. He and his priest stole the public money and hid it in a safe place. People were upset when they found the money missing. There was a great uproar. They wanted to know who had stolen the money. The minister with the special powers was called upon. He immediately knew who the culprits were but did not divulge their names. But the people were adamant to know their names. Finally, the minister divulged the names. People were shocked to know that it was the king himself and his priest. They were so mad at the pair that they banished them from the kingdom. After that, they made the minister their king and he ruled justly.

114. The Snake and the Foolish Disciple

Once, a teacher had many disciples. Among them was a foolish disciple. The teacher thought, 'Every being can learn. I am sure I can make this disciple a learned man.' One day, the teacher saw a snake and said to the foolish disciple, "Look! This snake looks like a long rope." The teacher made this comparison to show the length of the snake. The foolish disciple kept quiet.

One day, the teacher asked the foolish disciple to get him a long rope. The foolish disciple came back after a couple of hours. He handed out a snake to his teacher. The teacher was working, so he took the snake without looking. But, he immediately realised that it was not a rope. He was shocked to see the snake and immediately threw it away. He screamed, "Just because I told you that a snake looks like a rope, you brought a snake instead of a rope. Alas, you will remain foolish always!"

115. The Mischievous Spirit

Once, there was a great disciple of Lord Buddha. One night, he was in deep meditation under a tree. His bald head shone in the bright moonlight. A spirit saw this shining bald head and mischief struck him. He thought, 'I will break this monk's concentration by hitting him hard on the head.' So, it flew down and struck a heavy blow on the monk's head. The blow could have crumbled a mountain but it did not have any effect on the monk's head. The spirit was surprised. The monk could feel only a mild headache after finishing his meditation. The spirit realised that this was no ordinary monk. It flew down and said to the monk, "Sir, I wish to apologise, for I struck a blow on your head." The monk looked at it and smiled. He forgave the spirit immediately.

62

116. The Royal Horse

A royal horse was taken to a pool to be washed. Now, just before the arrival of the royal horse, a filthy horse had been washed there. The royal horse sniffed the air and knew that the pool was dirty and stinking. He turned up his nose in disgust and refused to get washed. The grooms complained to the king that the royal horse was being stubborn. Now, the king had a minister who understood animals. The king told him to sort out the matter. The king was worried that the horse might be sick.

The minister went to the pool. He found the horse perfectly healthy. He saw the unclean pool and guessed everything. Then, he told the grooms, "He is a fine horse and loves cleanliness. Take him to a clean place and give him a bath." The minister went to the king and said, "Sir, the horse is absolutely fine. It is indeed a royal horse." The king rewarded the minister.

117. The Ascetic Who Ate the Lizard's Flesh

Once, a great spirit resided in the form of a lizard. An ascetic built his hut where the lizard lived. The lizard, seeing the ascetic, went and paid its respects to the ascetic every day. But this ascetic was a rogue. He loved eating an animal's flesh. His weakness was a lizard's flesh. When he saw the lizard visiting him every day, he decided to catch it and enjoy its flesh. So, the next day, the ascetic waited for the lizard. But he was in for a surprise. As soon as the lizard entered the hut, it knew what was going to happen. It immediately turned back and started moving out of the door. The ascetic, in panic, threw his club at the lizard but missed it. The club, in turn, bounced back and hit the ascetic instead. The ascetic was badly wounded.

118. A Boy Helps the Ants

An army of ants lived in an anthill near a stream. Once it rained so heavily that the stream crossed its danger mark. The ants became worried that their anthill would get destroyed. So, they decided to leave the anthill. They took their food and started marching out of the anthill. But they came to a halt because outside the anthill was a puddle of water. The ants were dismayed. They knew they would be drowned if they entered the puddle. Now, a boy had been watching the activities of the ants. He could see what was bothering them. He immediately broke a big leaf from a tree and laid it on the puddle. The ants saw the leaf and immediately got onto it. Thus, they crossed over the puddle without any danger. They were highly indebted to the boy for his help and thanked him.

119. Never Trust a Chameleon

A group of iguanas lived in a forest. The iguana king's son was very friendly with a chameleon. The king did not like this and warned his son, "Chameleons are lowly creatures and cannot be trusted. They will bring trouble. Keep away from them." But the son ignored his warning. The king warned him repeatedly but had the same result. With the passage of time, the iguana grew in size but the chameleon remained the same. One day, the chameleon thought, 'He is becoming bigger and bigger. One day, he will crush me. I have to destroy him and his tribe before he gets me destroyed.' So, he went to an iguana hunter and told him where the iguanas lived. The hunter came and killed all the iguanas. Only the king escaped. He lamented over the death of his kith and kin and said, "One should never make friends with a chameleon, for he has caused our downfall."

120. Looks Can be Deceptive

A king was sitting near his window when he saw a very shabbily dressed woman on the road. She had a small bag of eatables in her hand. After some time, the king saw an old beggar near the woman who seemed to be thirsty and looking for water. Suddenly, the beggar fainted. The shabbily dressed woman saw this and brought water from a nearby well and sprinkled it on the beggar's face. The beggar became conscious. Then the woman gave him water to drink. After a while, the beggar got ready to move. The woman gave him her bag of eatables. The beggar thanked the woman and went away. The king called the woman in his palace and said, "You have a very kind heart. I was impressed with what you did out there. Will you marry me?" The woman was shocked at first but agreed later.

121. The Devoted Naga Wife

Once, there was a Naga king. He was married to a beautiful Naga princess. They lived happily together. But after some time, the Naga king was tired of his luxurious life and left his wife to meditate in the forest. While he was deep in meditation, a snake charmer caught him. He took him to several places and made the Naga king dance to his tunes. The Naga king's wife, in the meanwhile, left her palace to search for her husband. She kept searching him for years and finally found him dancing in a king's palace. She was full of tears when she saw her husband. Then she told the king everything about herself and the Naga king. The king immediately ordered the release of the Naga king. The wife was happy and took the Naga king home.

122. The Foolish Goat

A goat and an ass were bitter enemies. They always wanted to fight each other.

The goat thought, 'My horns are stronger than the ass's soft head. I can win a fight easily.'

So one day, the goat and the ass faced each other. The goat at once rushed forward, with his horns pointing straight at the ass.

Suddenly, the ass turned around and kicked back his hoofs with all his power. His hoofs hit the goat hard. But the goat's horns hurt the ass's legs as well.

From that day, they decided not to fight any more.

123. The Fox and the Drum

Once, a fox was searching around for food. He came across a hen and wanted to eat her. So, he hid himself in a bush and as he was going to pounce on her, he heard a strange tapping sound. Now, unknown to him, there was a drum in the tree. When the wind blew, the branches beat against it.

The greedy fox thought, 'There must be a bigger prey in the tree. I will eat that instead of the hen.'

He climbed up the tree making so much noise that the poor hen ran away. Expecting to find tasty prey, the greedy fox was disappointed to find a drum among the leaves.

The fox exclaimed, "I have been foolish. I let the hen get away because of my greed. Now, I will have to sleep on an empty stomach."

124. The Umbrella and the Single-Soled Shoes

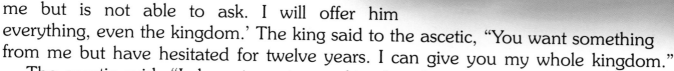

An ascetic, who was the guest of a king, thought of returning to his hermitage. But, he needed an umbrella and a pair of single-soled shoes. He decided to ask the king for those but thought, 'What if the king refuses to give me those? I will not be able to bear that and our friendship will also break.' So, he kept quiet. Twelve years passed by. One day, the king thought, 'There is something the ascetic wants from me but is not able to ask. I will offer him everything, even the kingdom.' The king said to the ascetic, "You want something from me but have hesitated for twelve years. I can give you my whole kingdom."

The ascetic said, "I do not want your kingdom but a pair of single-soled shoes and an umbrella. I could not ask you because I thought if you refused, I would be shattered and our friendship would break." The king fulfilled his needs and bade a tearful goodbye.

125. The Gifts

Long ago, there lived a monk. He used to give sermons to people. One day, pleased with his selfless acts, the queen gave him many gifts. After this, the king also gifted him many gifts. The monk gave away all the gifts to a young monk. This young monk, in turn, gave away the gifts to the other monks of his monastery. But

the monks were very angry. They felt jealous of the fact that the monk had given all the gifts to the young monk and not to them. They went and complained to their teacher about this. Their teacher replied, "The young monk has always helped the monk in times of need. So, he repaid the monk." The monks were ashamed of being jealous of the young monk and promised not to draw conclusions without knowing the facts.

126. The Wild Horses

Once, a cunning king possessed a wild horse. One day, a horse seller came to sell his horses. The cunning king did not want to pay a high price for the horses, so he asked his courtier to set the wild horse free among them. The wild horse bit the horses and wounded them. After that the king bought the horses at a low price. One of the king's ministers was very honest. He told the horse seller what the king did. The horse seller was angry. The minister asked him to get a wild horse the next time he came.

When the horse seller came again, he brought a wild horse with him. The king, as usual, set his wild horse free. But this time, the wild horse, to the king's surprise, got friendly with the other wild horse. The honest minister explained, "Sir, they got friendly because of their similar nature." The king had to give the right price for the horses and admitted his mistake.

127. The Barber's Son

A barber used to serve the royal families. One day, the barber came to the palace with his son. His son saw a beautiful girl in the garden and fell in love with her immediately. When they went home, the son told his father about the girl. The son said, "Father, I want to marry that girl." His father said, "We are from a different class and that girl is from a different class. It will not be possible." But the son refused to listen to his father. He stopped eating and drinking. Many people tried to persuade him to change his mind but he refused. After a few days, due to starvation, the son died. Many days later, the barber went to Lord Buddha and told him everything. Lord Buddha replied, "This was bound to happen as your son wanted something he could never have."

128. *The Two Friends*

Once, a royal priest's son and the prince were good friends. But when the prince grew up, he became wicked. He planned to kill his father and become the king. He shared his plan with his friend. The priest's son tried to persuade the prince from giving up his plan but the prince did not listen. As a result, the priest's son went to the forest and became an ascetic. Meanwhile, the prince killed his father but lost his peace of mind. He missed his friend and wanted to meet him. But, it was only after fifty years that the ascetic came to the kingdom and met him. The king asked his friend about the consequences of

his acts. The ascetic told him the horrors that awaited him in hell for his wicked acts. The king was horrified. Then the ascetic also told him that he could mend his ways and possibly go to the world of divine beings. As a result, the king mended his ways.

129. *Forgiveness*

There were two brothers. Their parents wanted them to settle down but they refused. They wanted to become ascetics. When their parents heard this, they suggested that they would all become ascetics. Once decided, they renounced the world and started living in the mountains. One day, the elder brother told the younger brother to bring ripe fruit for

their parents. But the younger son brought unripe fruit which made the elder son angry. He dismissed the younger brother. So, the brother went away. He met the king and helped him to defeat his enemies with his magical powers. The younger brother asked the king to help him get his brother's forgiveness. They went to the hermitage. The younger brother begged his brother's forgiveness. His brother forgave him and they all lived happily together.

130. True Love

Once, the god of birds fell in love with a queen. He disguised himself as a handsome young man and started playing dice with the queen's husband. One day, the young man decided to marry the queen. So, using his powers, he carried her away to his kingdom. The king was very distressed when he found his wife missing. He called his minister and told him to search for his wife. Meanwhile, the young man came every day to play dice with the unsuspecting king. On the other hand, the minister searched high and low for the queen. Ultimately, he found her. He brought her safely back to the king. The king was very happy and there were tears of joy in his eyes. The god of birds realised what he had done was wrong. He went away and never came back.

131. The Fox and the Crow

A crow was sitting on a tree with some meat in its beak. A hungry fox saw the crow and felt very jealous. He thought of a plan to steal the meat.

He said, 'Dear Crow, how beautiful you look today! With your shining feathers and melodious voice, you should be crowned the king of birds.'

The crow was flattered and wanted to show off its voice. It tried to caw loudly and dropped the meat from its beak.

The fox quickly gobbled it up and said, 'Crow, you have a loud voice but you have no brain!'

132. The Humble Prince

Once, a prince of a mighty kingdom was walking down a road. While walking, he overlooked a poor Brahmin sitting on the pavement and knocked him over. In the process, the Brahmin's bowl also broke and his alms lay scattered everywhere. The prince was very ashamed of his act and said to the Brahmin, "Sir! I am very sorry. I am the prince of this kingdom. Come to me for help when you need." Saying so, the prince left. Many years later, the prince became the king. One day, while he was taking a round of his kingdom, a Brahmin came and stood in front of his chariot. The king recognised him immediately as the poor man whom he had knocked off many years back. He immediately got down from his chariot and gave the Brahmin lots of precious gifts and wealth.

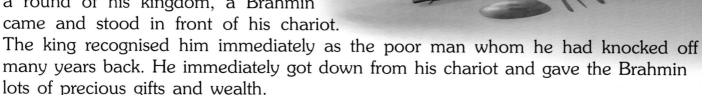

133. The Lying Jackal

Once, in a forest, there lived two friends-a tiger and a lion. A jackal used to feed on whatever food was left by the two. One day, he thought, "I have never eaten the flesh of a tiger or a lion before. What if I get them to fight each other? In the process, they will kill each other and I will have a feast." Thinking so, he first went to the tiger and said, "The lion is saying bad things about you." Then he went to the lion and said the same thing there. But he was in for a surprise as his plan did not work out. The tiger and the lion discussed what the jackal had said. They realised that the jackal had been lying. The jackal could do nothing else but run to save his life. The lion and the tiger had a good laugh over this.

134. *The Archer's Fear*

One day, seven kings decided to attack the younger brother's kingdom.

The younger brother got frightened. He called for his brother as he was incapable of protecting the kingdom himself. The elder brother immediately came back.

He reassured his brother that he would not let anything happen to the kingdom.

Then, he took an arrow and scratched a message on it which said, "I, the elder prince, have returned. I will kill you all with one arrow." He shot such an arrow that it fell upon the very middle of a golden dish from which the seven kings were eating together.

The seven kings were so frightened that they ran away.

Thus, without shedding even a drop of blood, the elder brother made the enemy run.

Later, the elder brother renounced the world and became an ascetic.

135. *The Great Archer*

A king had two sons. The elder one became an expert in archery.

The king wanted him to become the king but he refused and made the younger one the king.

But one day, one of the servants poisoned the younger brother's ears by saying, "Your elder brother wants to be the king." He believed the servant and sent some men to imprison the elder brother.

But the elder brother went away to another country and became a royal archer.

He performed great feats with his archery. The king and the people of that kingdom were mesmerised.

They praised and gave precious gifts to him. The king became a great fan of his. The elder son's name spread far and wide. He was known as the master of archery.

136. The Good Advice

A man had three daughters. They were very beautiful and noble. They all were of marriageable age. The man was confused. He did not know what kind of groom to choose for each of them. One day, an ascetic came to his house. The man asked him, "Sir, what kind of groom do I choose for each of my daughters? Should he be handsome or noble or virtuous?" The ascetic replied, "Well, good looks never last forever and are of no use. Nobility is not a guarantee that the groom will be noble. The only thing that matters is being virtuous. A man is remembered for his good virtues even after he passes away." The man was pleased with the answer. He thanked the ascetic for his valuable advice. Soon, he chose three virtuous grooms for his three daughters.

137. Guessing the Name

Once, an ascetic found a lotus flower larger than its actual size. He had a doubt that something was in the flower. He found a baby in a lotus flower. The ascetic tended her as his daughter. She became very beautiful over the years. Rumours of her beauty spread far. A king came to seek her hand from the ascetic. The ascetic said, "You can marry her if you can guess her name."

The ascetic had named her Ashanka, meaning doubt, as he was not sure what was in the lotus flower.

The king agreed. From that day, he kept thinking about the girl's name. One day, the girl gave him a hint but the king could still not get the answer.

Many years passed by. The king was almost going to give up when the girl again gave him a hint. This time the king guessed the name. He told the ascetic, "Her name is Ashanka."

The ascetic gave away his daughter as promised to the king.

138. *The Price of Greed*

There was a sailor who loved exploring new lands. One day, he came upon a beautiful island. This island had delicious fruits. The sailor enjoyed himself but his greed for more made him sail away.

Next, he reached a land which was full of good food and wine. The sailor spent some days there but again set off to explore newer regions. Soon, he came to a land of fairies and precious stones. The fairies treated him like an emperor fulfilling his every wish.

But, the sailor's curiosity was not satisfied and he again set off to find a new land. This time the sailor came to hell. He saw a man in iron chains there. The sailor, having only gone through good times, thought the chains to be of gold. He unfastened the chains and wore them himself. But as soon as he did that, he realised he was in hell and was to suffer forever. He repented on his greediness.

139. *Being Good*

A king's chief priest was respected by everyone. The priest thought, "Am I respected because of my birth or my knowledge or my goodness?" He decided to find out. He went to the royal coin maker and picked up a coin. The coin maker did not say anything. The priest repeated this thrice. The third time the coin maker shouted, "You are a thief and all the while I thought you were a good man." The coin maker decided to take the priest to the king. On the way, the priest saw a snake charmer. The priest warned the snake charmer to be careful of snakes but the snake charmer retorted, "The nature of snakes is not hidden from anyone. We need to be safe from people like you who appear to be good but are evil from inside." The priest realised that being good was admired the most. He told the king everything. The king released him and he resumed his duty.

140. The Earth Falling Apart

Once, a hare was resting under a tree when a thought occurred to him, 'What if the earth gets destroyed? What would happen to me?' Suddenly, a big fruit fell from the tree with a thud. The hare thought, 'The earth is falling apart.' Without looking back, he started running out of fear. Another hare saw him running in fear and asked, "Why are you scared and running?" The hare replied, "The earth is falling apart." The other hares also started running. After that many other animals joined in.

A wise lion saw them running. He asked them what the matter was. All of them replied, "The earth is falling apart." The lion asked, "Who saw it falling apart?"

The hare came forward and told him everything.

The lion went to the place where the hare had rested and found a big fruit on the ground. He understood everything and told the animals the reality. The animals were embarrassed about their foolishness.

141. The Clever Monkey

A large number of monkeys lived together with their leader. One day, it was very hot and the monkeys were very thirsty. They found a lake which was very beautiful. The monkeys were very happy and decided to jump into the lake. But before they could do so, their leader stopped them. He warned them, "Wait. Do not hurry. This place is new. We must be careful and check out the area."

Saying so, the monkey leader looked around and found that there were many footprints on the sand. All these footprints led to the lake but none came back from it. The monkey leader became suspicious and realised that a demon must be dwelling in the lake, so it was not wise to dive into the lake. He told the other monkeys to drink water by using bamboos as straws and sucking water from the lake. All the monkeys easily quenched their thirst by using bamboos.

142. The Faithful Parrot

A parrot used to live on a fig tree. He loved the figs and enjoyed living on the tree. Time passed by. After several years, the fig tree stopped bearing fruit. It had become old now. The parrot felt sad but did not leave the tree.

God saw this. He disguised himself as a bird and asked the parrot, "Why do you not leave this tree? It is not bearing fruit anymore."

The parrot replied, "I cannot leave my friend. It has fed me for so many years."

God was happy to hear this answer. He came to his original form and said to the parrot, "You faithfulness to the tree has impressed me. Ask me what you want."

The parrot replied, "O Lord! Bless the tree to bear fruit again like it did before."

God did as was asked. And lo! The tree was full of fruit. The tree was very happy and thanked the parrot and God.

143. Who is the Prettier?

Once, two fish lived in separate rivers. They both were pretty. One day, by chance, they met each other. The first fish said, "Hello! I think you come from another river as I have never seen you before." The second fish replied, "Yes, I live in another river." After introducing themselves, the fish started talking. After some time, the first fish said, "Look at me. I am very pretty. Do you not think so?" The second fish replied, "Yes, you are. But I am also very pretty. In fact, I am prettier than you. Everyone says I am the prettiest fish in the world." After that both got into an argument over who was the prettier. They could not solve the issue. Suddenly, they saw a tortoise coming towards them. The first fish called out to him and said, "Sir! Please tell us which of us is the prettier?" The tortoise replied, "Both of you are pretty but I am the prettiest." The fish were astounded.

144. The Wise Goose

Long ago, there was a flock of geese led by a wise leader. A king, impressed by the wise goose, became its friend. They used to meet every day and talk of many things.

Now, one day, two young geese got into an argument as to who was the faster. They decided to race against the sun to prove who was the faster. The wise goose warned them that they would not be able to catch up with the sun but they did not listen. They flew towards the sun and kept trying to catch up with it but could not. Slowly, they got tired and weak. The wise goose brought them down. After that the wise goose itself raced against the sun and won. The king, who saw all this, congratulated the goose. He, then, asked the goose, "Is there anything faster than you?" The goose replied, "Yes, there is. It is time. Time never stops for anyone. Everything decays with time."

145. The Noble Elephant

An elephant king had six tusks. He had two wives. One day, the elephant, by accident, hit a tree with his trunk. In the process, flowers fell on the first wife and red ants fell on the second wife. The second wife thought the elephant loved the first wife more. She left her husband forever.

In her second birth, she became a queen. But she had not forgotten her insult in the previous birth. She wanted revenge and asked her husband to get her the elephant's six tusks. A hunter was sent for the task. He wounded the elephant. But still, the elephant fought bravely. The hunter was impressed and told the elephant everything. The elephant realised that the queen was his wife. He cut off his tusks and gave them to the hunter and died after some time. The hunter, with a heavy heart, gave the tusks to the queen and told her everything. The queen realised her mistake and died of grief.

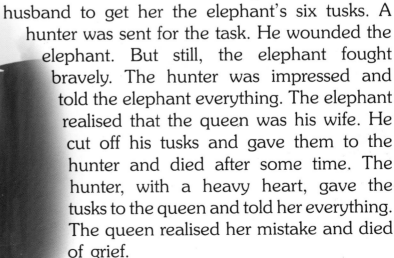

146. *The Young Priest*

A priest, who performed the royal ceremonies in a kingdom, passed away. His young son became the priest. Now, the festival of elephants was fast approaching, so the other priests went to the king and said, "Your Majesty, the priest in-charge is too young to perform the ceremony. Let us handle the ceremony." The king agreed. When the young priest told his mother about this, she cried, "This place is rightfully yours after your father's death. You should perform the ceremony."

The young priest went to a learned teacher and asked him to teach him all about the elephant festival. The teacher having heard everything started teaching the young priest. The young priest learnt everything very quickly.

On the day of the festival, he went to the king and said, "I know everything about the festival. Do not disinherit me of my right. He challenged the other priests with his knowledge and they could not defeat him."

Finally, the king gave the young priest his right.

147. *The Selfish Man*

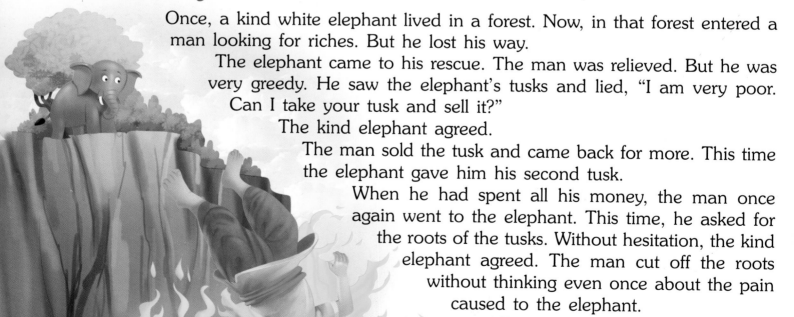

Once, a kind white elephant lived in a forest. Now, in that forest entered a man looking for riches. But he lost his way.

The elephant came to his rescue. The man was relieved. But he was very greedy. He saw the elephant's tusks and lied, "I am very poor. Can I take your tusk and sell it?"

The kind elephant agreed.

The man sold the tusk and came back for more. This time the elephant gave him his second tusk.

When he had spent all his money, the man once again went to the elephant. This time, he asked for the roots of the tusks. Without hesitation, the kind elephant agreed. The man cut off the roots without thinking even once about the pain caused to the elephant.

But the gods above were not happy to see this selfish act. They were so angry that the earth trembled and cracked open. Flames of fire ate up the selfish man.

148. The Servant and the Treasure

A rich old man had a son whom he loved very much. One day, the old man died.

The old man's wise friend told the son, "Your father buried his wealth deep in the forest. Only your servant knows its location."

The son took the servant with him to bring the wealth. When they reached the forest, the servant did a weird thing. He started insulting the son.

The son was puzzled by the servant's strange behaviour. This happened again and again.

He went to his father's wise friend to seek his advice.

The wise old man said, "Take the servant to the forest again. Observe where he stands when he insults you. Dig up the ground on that very spot and you will find the wealth.

Your servant becomes proud that he is the only one who knows the spot. So, he misuses this feeling by insulting you."

The son followed the advice. And lo! He found the wealth.

149. The Man Who Sold the Dead Mouse

Once, a man overheard another man saying, "A man can build a fortune even from such small beginnings as this dead mouse." Now, this man was none other than the king's adviser.

The man decided to act on his words. He picked the mouse that the adviser pointed to.

As soon as he picked the dead mouse, a shopkeeper bought the mouse for two copper coins.

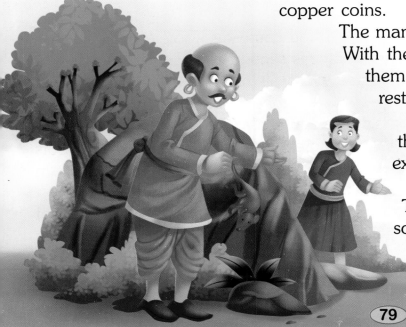

The man bought sweets with the coins and sold them. With the money earned, he bought flowers and sold them. He earned so much that he opened a restaurant.

He became very rich in time. He wanted to thank the adviser for this. He sent a very expensive gift to the adviser.

The adviser asked him the reason for this. The man told him everything. The adviser was so impressed that he married his daughter to the man. When the adviser passed away, the man became the adviser to the king.

150. *The Foolish Trees*

Long ago, trees could talk. One day, they were having an angry discussion. A fir tree said, "All the animals come and rest under us and dirty the area."

The pine tree said angrily, "Let us teach them a lesson that they will not forget!"

A wise old banyan tree said, "Calm down, my friend. You will fall into trouble if the animals go away."

But the pine tree was adamant. The other trees also agreed with it. So, when the animals came there, the trees moved so fiercely that all the animals got frightened and ran away.

The trees were very happy. They enjoyed the calm and serene atmosphere.

But there was trouble ahead. Suddenly, two woodcutters approached the trees.

One said to the other, "Finally, there are no animals here. Now, we can easily cut the trees."

The other replied, "Yes, my friend."

Saying so, they started chopping the pine tree. The other trees could only watch in despair.

151. *The Turtle Who Opened His Mouth*

A turtle and two geese were great friends.

One day, one of the geese said to the turtle, "We are going to our homeland tomorrow. Will you come with us?"

The turtle said, "I cannot fly like you."

The goose said, "Do not worry. We have a plan."

The geese brought a stick. They held the ends of it. Then they said to the turtle, "Take the middle of the stick in your mouth. Keep holding it and do not open your mouth." The turtle agreed.

Soon, the geese were flying in the air with the turtle.

Some children saw them and made fun of the turtle.

The turtle could not keep quiet and opened his mouth to reply. As soon as he opened his mouth, he fell down and died.

The geese mourned the loss of their friend and exclaimed, "If only he had not opened his mouth!"